YORK NOTES

The Mayor of Casterbridge

Thomas Hardy

Notes by Mary Sewell

 Longman   York Press

YORK PRESS
322 Old Brompton Road, London SW5 9JH

Pearson Education Limited
Edinburgh Gate, Harlow,
Essex CM20 2JE, United Kingdom
Associated companies, branches and representatives throughout the world

First published 1997
Fourth impression 1999
ISBN 0-582-31426-7

Designed by Vicki Pacey, Trojan Horse
Illustrated by Adam Stower
Map by Martin Ursell
Typeset by Pantek Arts, Maidstone, Kent
Phototypeset by Gem Graphics, Trenance, Mawgan Porth, Cornwall
Colour reproduction and film output by Spectrum Colour
Produced by Addison Wesley Longman China Limited, Hong Kong

ONTENTS

PREFACE

York Notes are designed to give you a broader perspective on works of literature studied at GCSE and equivalent levels. We have carried out extensive research into the needs of the modern literature student prior to publishing this new edition. Our research showed that no existing series fully met students' requirements. Rather than present a single authoritative approach, we have provided alternative viewpoints, empowering students to reach their own interpretations of the text. York Notes provide a close examination of the work and include biographical and historical background, summaries, glossaries, analyses of characters, themes, structure and language, cultural connections and literary terms.

If you look at the Contents page you will see the structure for the series. However, there's no need to read from the beginning to the end as you would with a novel, play, poem or short story. Use the Notes in the way that suits you. Our aim is to help you with your understanding of the work, not to dictate how you should learn.

York Notes are written by English teachers and examiners, with an expert knowledge of the subject. They show you how to succeed in coursework and examination assignments, guiding you through the text and offering practical advice. Questions and comments will extend, test and reinforce your knowledge. Attractive colour design and illustrations improve clarity and understanding, making these Notes easy to use and handy for quick reference.

York Notes are ideal for:

- Essay writing
- Exam preparation
- Class discussion

The author of these Notes is Mary Sewell MA, B Ed, an assistant examiner for GCSE English, former Head of English Faculty, co-ordinator of the National Oracy Project, and advisory teacher for English in County Durham. She is now a part-time lecturer in Education at Durham University and a tutor for the Open University.

The text used in these notes is the Longman Literature Edition, edited by Paul Roberts.

Health Warning: **This study guide will enhance your understanding, but should not replace the reading of the original text and/or study in class.**

PART ONE

INTRODUCTION

HOW TO STUDY A NOVEL

You have bought this book because you wanted to study a novel on your own. This may supplement classwork.

- You will need to read the novel several times. Start by reading it quickly for pleasure, then read it slowly and carefully. Further readings will generate new ideas and help you to memorise the details of the story.
- Make careful notes on themes, plot and characters of the novel. The plot will change some of the characters. Who changes?
- The novel may not present events chronologically. Does the novel you are reading begin at the beginning of the story or does it contain flashbacks and a muddled time sequence? Can you think why?
- How is the story told? Is it narrated by one of the characters or by an all-seeing ('omniscient') narrator?
- Does the same person tell the story all the way through? Or do we see the events through the minds and feelings of a number of different people.
- Which characters does the narrator like? Which characters do you like or dislike? Do your sympathies change during the course of the book? Why? When?
- Any piece of writing (including your notes and essays) is the result of thousands of choices. No book had to be written in just one way: could the author could have chosen other words, other phrases, other characters, other events. How could the author of your novel have written the story differently? If events were recounted by a minor character how would this change the novel?

Studying on your own requires self-discipline and a carefully thought-out work plan in order to be effective. Good luck.

Childhood

Thomas Hardy was born 2 June 1840, son of a stone mason, in a small village called Higher Bockhampton, three miles east of Dorchester. Dorchester is used for Casterbridge in *The Mayor of Casterbridge*, well drawn by Hardy because he was able to convey what he observed, heard and felt for himself. Dorchester was the most important town in the area and Hardy was educated here; walking from a young age to and from school. He had ample time to observe not only the physical surroundings but also the people.

Studies

As soon as Thomas was seventeen he became articled to John Hicks, an architect in Dorchester. It was in this job that the young Hardy met the Reverend Moule, the vicar of Fordington. He used Fordington as Durnover in *The Mayor of Casterbridge*, and used Mill Lane in Fordington as Mixen Lane. Part of his studies involved learning Greek and Latin and the difficult course Hardy undertook is perhaps reflected in the difficulties Elizabeth-Jane in the novel also had in learning these languages.

Hardy the architect

When Hardy completed his training in 1862 he moved to London but did not like the boring and repetitive tasks necessary to become a successful and ambitious architect. Hardy gave these qualities, the ones he himself lacked, to Farfrae and made this character a successful businessman. Hardy turned increasingly to literature, writing poems instead of concentrating on architectural drawings.

Marriage

By 1867 Hardy was becoming increasingly depressed and returned to Dorchester to take up a job with his former employer Hicks. A few years later Hardy was sent to supervise work at St Juliot's Church near Boscastle in Cornwall, and here he met and fell in love with and married Emma Lavinia Gifford. Here, too, Hardy wrote *Far from the Madding Crowd*, another novel centred around Casterbridge. In 1883, he returned to live in Dorchester and began writing *The Mayor of Casterbridge* in a serialised form, published weekly in *The Graphic* in 1886.

Hardy and his wife, who were not always happy, moved to live in Max Gate. Hardy visited London frequently and mixed with the literary and socially famous. Further novels by him appeared – *Tess of the D'Urbervilles* and *Jude the Obscure* – but his work reflected views which were considered outrageous and immoral for the time. Hardy decided to write poetry instead.

Emma Hardy died in 1912, and some of Hardy's finest poetry was produced whilst in a highly emotive state following her death.

Second marriage

In 1914 he married Florence Dugdale, an authoress of children's stories. Florence was much younger than Thomas, but an attachment developed between them as she worked for him as his secretary, Hardy's home Max Gate became an energetic centre for writers. Many famous authors such as Virginia Woolf, Siegfried Sassoon and H.G. Wells visited Hardy and exchanged ideas.

Hardy went on to write well into his old age, planning to publish a volume to celebrate his ninetieth birthday. Sadly in later years he became depressed and disillusioned with the events of the First World War.

Hardy died in 1928; his heart was interred in Stinsford churchyard near Dorchester, in the grave of his first wife, and his ashes taken to Westminster Abbey for a state funeral.

Hardy, who was born only three years after Queen Victoria came to the throne, and was still alive during the reign of Edward VII and George V, was able to see many social changes actually take place. His life covered one of the most exciting periods of technical and scientific advancement and *The Mayor of Casterbridge* reflects some of these.

The Mayor of Casterbridge, although published in 1886, is set in the years before the Corn Laws. Hardy experienced the Crimean War, the Indian Mutiny, the Boer War and the Great War during his lifetime, and these political changes juxtaposed with technological advancement made his reflections back to 1815 even more poignant.

The Corn Laws

In 1815 British farmers enjoyed immense prosperity, since the Corn Law imposed heavy duties on the imports of foreign corn, and these were not repealed until 1846. Wealthy farmers and merchants who had flourished were, however, in the process of changing the style of their business. Up to this time many businesses were family-run concerns and bargains were made by word of mouth; but now a move to ordered systems and bookkeeping was becoming a necessity. We see these differences in the early conversation between Henchard and Farfrae. Henchard represented the old-style trader and Farfrae the new businessman.

Mechanisation

Men were being replaced by machines, which were both cheaper and more efficient. Traditionally people had worked where they lived; now men moved to larger towns or even emigrated. Smaller businesses were taken over by co-operative groups and smaller farms by larger ones. The whole notion of working in small units was vanishing.

Social values   Values and attitudes were also changing. In 1859
Charles Darwin published his revolutionary book, *On
the Origin of Species* which undermined fundamental
assumptions and values. The Church was divided by
those who believed in the Bible literally and those who
interpreted its teachings in a more liberal and
humanitarian way. *The Mayor of Casterbridge* gives us
some insight into 'proper' and 'improper' behaviour and
we have a taste of how Victorian audiences would be
shocked at the revelations of Henchard, Susan, and
Lucetta, all of whom in their different ways broke
'God's laws'. Religion was vitally important; all attended
church on Sundays and Henchard swore his oath inside
a church and stuck to his vows.

Rural life   In *The Mayor of Casterbridge* Hardy also manages to
capture the essence of rural life, gossip, superstition and
pagan customs. Hardy describes the 'skimmington-ride'
as being an acceptable custom; punishment was meted
out to those who deserved it and public ridicule was a
natural part of justice. The hiring of servants on Old
Candlemas Day and the consultation of the old
'weather-prophet', fate and rituals were all features of
rural life at this time.

Hardy uses real places to describe Casterbridge and the
surrounding area. Weyhill is Weydon-Priors.
Dorchester is Casterbridge, and many of the features
described by Hardy can still be found today: Henchard's
house is said to be where the present Barclay's Bank
stands in Dorchester. The detailed description of the
Ring and the Roman amphitheatre give us a clear
feeling of the effect of historical buildings which add to
the ambience of the novel.

PART TWO

SUMMARIES

GENERAL SUMMARY

Chapters 1–5: Around the year 1820 Henchard along with his wife
To and baby daughter are walking wearily towards
Casterbridge Weydon-Priors, where he hopes to find work as a hay-
they go trusser. They come across a fair and Henchard becomes
drunk in the furmity tent and sells his wife and
daughter in an auction to a sailor, Richard Newson.
This trio leaves and emigrates to Canada. Next day,
Henchard searches for his wife, but in vain. He swears
an oath not to drink alcohol for twenty-one years.

Chapters 6–12: Some eighteen years later Susan with her daughter
A family Elizabeth-Jane return to the fairground and make
reunited enquiries about Henchard. At the direction of the
furmity woman the two women go to Casterbridge and
see Henchard there, not only a thriving businessman
but also mayor. The story of the auction has been kept
from Elizabeth-Jane, who thinks of her father as
Newson, now believed drowned.

The same evening a Scotsman, Donald Farfrae, sends a
note to Mayor Henchard offering his services on a
problem of overgrown grain. The two women find
themselves sharing the same inn with Farfrae, and
Elizabeth-Jane feels an attraction towards him.
Henchard visits Farfrae and offers him a job. Susan is
able to overhear all the conversation through the wall.

Susan meets Henchard in secret the following day. He
plans to take a cottage for her and Elizabeth-Jane, visit
them there, and eventually 'marry' Susan publicly to put
matters right.

Henchard confides the story of Susan, and his liaison
with Lucetta, a young woman from Jersey, to Farfrae.

Henchard had genuinely believed Susan to be dead, and has promised marriage to Lucetta. Farfrae helps Henchard write a letter to Lucetta explaining the situation and breaking off the engagement. Farfrae is now Henchard's manager, and is bringing new methods to the business.

Chapters 13–22:
A marriage, a death, and another reunion

Henchard and Susan marry.

Henchard wants Elizabeth-Jane to be called Henchard, but Susan has a word with Elizabeth-Jane and cautions her against this. Farfrae and Elizabeth-Jane seem to be attracted to one another after being sent to a barn by an unknown note-sender.

Rivalry develops between Farfrae and Henchard.

Susan becomes ill, and Lucetta writes to Henchard requesting her love letters be returned. Lucetta has inherited her aunt's estate and has changed her name to Templeman. Susan dies leaving a letter that is to be opened on Elizabeth-Jane's wedding day, but Henchard reads it and discovers that Elizabeth-Jane is Newson's child. He cannot overcome his feelings and he treats Elizabeth-Jane indifferently and harshly. He gives Farfrae permission see Elizabeth-Jane.

Chapters 23–33:
A secret marriage

Lucetta Templeman moves into High-Place Hall. Through an accidental meeting Elizabeth-Jane becomes her companion. Lucetta still hopes to marry Henchard.

Farfrae comes to High-Place Hall to visit Elizabeth-Jane, but falls in love with Lucetta; the attraction is mutual. Henchard fires Jopp as his manager. Overhearing a conversation between Lucetta and Farfrae discussing marriage, Henchard visits Lucetta and forcing Elizabeth-Jane to be a witness bullies Lucetta into promising marriage to him.

Henchard, sitting as magistrate, has to hear a case against the furmity woman. She recognises Henchard and tells the story of the auction to the courtroom. Elizabeth-Jane finds lodgings and watches Henchard's decline into bankruptcy – he is forced to sell everything and go to lodge with Jopp. Farfrae now owns Henchard's house and business. Henchard works for him trussing hay; he is back where he started.

Henchard's vow of sobriety finishes and after hearing the news that Farfrae is to become mayor, he starts to drink heavily.

Chapters
34–45:
The downfall
of Michael
Henchard

Lucetta still has not had her letters returned, and is now married to Farfrae. She writes again to Henchard. Henchard returns to his old home and reads extracts of the letters to Farfrae but does not disclose the writer. Henchard gives the letters to Jopp to take to Lucetta. Jopp reads them in a pub to the locals, who decide to produce a skimmington-ride to embarrass Henchard and Lucetta.

A royal person is due to visit Casterbridge, but Henchard is ignored and, slighted by Farfrae, is turned away from the celebrations. Henchard stages a fight which takes place in the granary. Henchard ties one arm behind his back to make the fight 'fair' but his intentions were to kill Farfrae. Henchard wins the fight but lets Farfrae go.

Farfrae is sent a note to take him to Weatherbury so that he will not see the skimmington-ride.

Lucetta sees the effigies of Henchard and herself from her window, has a massive fit and lies dangerously ill. Henchard runs to find Farfrae to persuade him to go home immediately; however, Farfrae does not believe Henchard and goes home two hours later, just before Lucetta dies.

Henchard becomes closer to Elizabeth-Jane, but Newson makes a reappearance. Henchard tells Newson that Elizabeth-Jane is dead. Newson goes away. Henchard, now suicidal, goes to drown himself, but sees the effigy of himself in the water, and decides against it. Newson reappears and Henchard, fearing the discovery of his lies, leaves Casterbridge.

Henchard stays within a fifty-mile radius of Casterbridge. He hears of Elizabeth-Jane's wedding and takes a caged bird to the house. Elizabeth-Jane, distressed at Henchard, has a row with him and sends him away.

The following morning Elizabeth-Jane bitterly regrets her harsh treatment of Henchard and is particularly sorry when she learns of the caged bird.

Farfrae starts a search for Henchard and discovers Abel Whittle, who tells them that Henchard has died. They all go to a derelict cottage where Henchard's body lies. Pinned to the bedhead is Henchard's will entreating that his memory be forgotten. The novel concludes with a brief description of Elizabeth-Jane growing to full maturity and becoming a well-balanced and valued member of the community.

Detailed Summaries

CHAPTER 1

Their silence born of 'stale frustration' indicates the state of their relationship.

An unemployed hay-trusser and his wife trudge towards Weydon-Priors. There is a fair in the village and the couple enter a furmity tent for refreshment, furmity being a nourishing, alcohol-free drink. However, with the hay-trusser's connivance, for 'the man as slily sent back money in payment', the furmity woman laces the brew with rum and the hay-trusser quickly becomes drunk. He offers to sell his wife by auction. At first he is not taken seriously, but he becomes more insistent and vehement, and eventually a sailor makes a bid of five guineas.

The woman and her baby go with the sailor; her husband is left in the tent to sleep off the alcohol.

COMMENT

The hay-trusser, who we learn later is Henchard, is a fine figure, 'a skilled countryman' carrying the tools of his trade. This contrasts with the 'disadvantaged shabbiness' of their dust-covered clothes and reflects their immediate distress.

Note the tender way the horses caress each other. Compare descriptions of the two auctions.

The furmity woman will make three more appearances, each one indicating a change in Henchard's fortunes.

A description of the horse auction outside the tent immediately before the auction of Susan parodies (see Literary Terms) the event.

The sailor Newson arrives fortuitously at the right moment. Susan is tired physically and emotionally. She throws her wedding ring back at her husband to signify the end of her marriage.

GLOSSARY

thimble-riggers conjurers

furmity a non-alcoholic drink made from wheat, raisins, spice and milk

keacorn throat

the great trumpet refers to the Day of Judgement

CHAPTER *2*

Henchard is shown in a more favourable light in this chapter.

Think why he goes into the church.

The following morning the young man awakes to find his wife's wedding ring and has only the vaguest recollection of the night before. He hastily leaves the fairground intending to find his wife and daughter, but searches in vain. Full of remorse he enters a church and swears an oath that he will not drink for twenty-one years. It is only here that we learn his name is Michael Henchard. He gives up his search when he learns that persons answering their description have emigrated.

COMMENT

Although Henchard regrets his actions, he seems more concerned with his reputation.

Henchard is torn between finding his wife and child, and enjoying his newfound freedom.

A monologue (see Literary Terms) is used to emphasise Henchard's superstitious nature. He required 'fit place and imagery' for swearing his oath. This rural naïveté is reflected in Susan's simplistic belief that having been sold at auction makes the deal binding.

TO CASTERBRIDGE THEY GO

GLOSSARY   **the Seven Sleepers had a dog** this refers to the story of Ephesus, where seven Christians hid in a cave and slept for 300 years
sacrarium part of church in front of altar
foot-pace where priest stands

CHAPTER 3

The journey in this chapter repeats that of Chapter 1.

Years later, Susan Henchard, now called Newson, and her grown-up daughter Elizabeth-Jane return to Weydon-Priors. The two turn aside at the fair and find the furmity woman, now in much reduced circumstances. Susan tells her she is in mourning for her husband lost at sea, and asks the furmity woman to cast her mind back eighteen years. The furmity woman is able to tell her that Henchard had returned to the fair a year after selling his wife.

COMMENT

These first two chapters form a prologue (see Literary Terms) to the novel.

The arrival of Susan and her daughter in Weydon-Priors is in stark contrast to the arrival of Henchard and Susan years before. Mother and daughter hold hands affectionately as they walk.

Hardy uses the symbols (see Literary Terms) of lonely figures in an open landscape to emphasise the effects of arranged or accidental meetings.

Susan has not told Elizabeth-Jane of her marriage to Henchard. This deception forms a major theme in the novel.

GLOSSARY   **withy** a willow
highfliers old-fashioned swings set in a frame
soi-disant self-styled, so-called

CHAPTER 4

We learn that Susan and the baby had been taken to Canada by Newson, returning to Falmouth about twelve years later. A friend of Susan's had set doubt into her mind about the legality of her marriage to Newson. When he is later reported lost at sea Susan decides to

The conversation between Susan and the baker (p. 29) enables us to understand Henchard.

search for Henchard. Susan wants a better life for Elizabeth-Jane, to improve her status from 'the strait-waistcoat of poverty' (p. 25).

When Susan and Elizabeth-Jane arrive in Casterbridge they find people complaining about inedible bread, a result of being sold sprouting wheat.

COMMENT

Susan believes that Newson had a 'morally real and justifiable right to her by his purchase' (p. 23) which helps us understand why she stayed with him.

Elizabeth-Jane, who 'sought further into things than other girls in her position ever did' (p. 25), seems to yearn for deeper learning rather than social advancement.

Casterbridge is described with its sights and sounds, its ruined Roman garrison and tree-lined avenues. Hardy emphasises its obvious reliance on agriculture, and carefully describes the architecture, giving us a picture not only of the town, but also, through use of dialect (see Literary Terms), a picture of its rural inhabitants.

GLOSSARY

carking distressing
champaign a level stretch of open countryside
brick-nogging bricks laid in patterns between the timber frames of a house
pattens shoes with wooden soles
Sicilian Mariner's Hymn hymn played by church bells
growed wheat sprouting wheat which is useless for baking
plim swell

TO CASTERBRIDGE THEY GO

CHAPTER 5

Compare the description of Henchard (p. 33) with that in Chapter 1 (p. 1).

The two women, attracted by the town band, find themselves outside The King's Arms. Local people are peering through the window at a banquet and at the mayor, Michael Henchard. Susan becomes nervous about approaching him. Henchard is drinking water although rum and wine are being served. The women quickly learn of his teetotal oath, which has two more years to run.

COMMENT

The portrayal of Henchard as wealthy and powerful is in dramatic (see Literary Terms) contrast to his last appearance as an out-of-work hay-trusser.

Henchard still has his volatile temper, only controlled by a skin-deep composure.

Note the time sequences. Henchard's oath has only two years to run and Elizabeth-Jane is eighteen years old, a fact which is to become more significant later.

GLOSSARY

fall a veil ladies wore over their faces

akin to a coach indicates wealth, in that he could afford to keep a coach

rummers large glasses

to-year this year

list a layer of unrisen dough which gives a leathery base to the loaf

A

Identify the speaker.

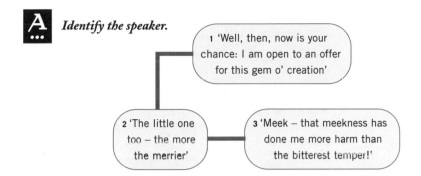

1 'Well, then, now is your chance: I am open to an offer for this gem o' creation'

2 'The little one too – the more the merrier'

3 'Meek – that meekness has done me more harm than the bitterest temper!'

Identify the person 'to whom' this comment refers.

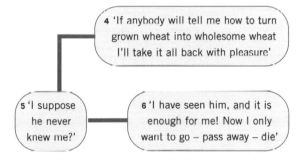

4 'If anybody will tell me how to turn grown wheat into wholesome wheat I'll take it all back with pleasure'

5 'I suppose he never knew me?'

6 'I have seen him, and it is enough for me! Now I only want to go – pass away – die'

Check your answers on page 87.

B

Consider these issues.

a Hardy uses the first two chapters as prologue to the story to build up the tension.

b Note the way in which Henchard has changed in the first five chapters.

c Look at the character of Susan Henchard. See what evidence there is in the text to support your own views.

d Think about what Hardy is telling us when he says the bread is inedible in Casterbridge.

A FAMILY REUNITED

CHAPTER 6

Letters and notes
play an important
part in this novel.

Donald Farfrae, a traveller, also hears Michael
Henchard saying that the 'grown' wheat cannot be used.
Acting on impulse, the young man sends Henchard a
note and then leaves to spend the night at The Three
Mariners inn.

Susan and Elizabeth-Jane are staying at the same inn,
and the chapter closes with Henchard going there to
find Farfrae.

COMMENT

Coincidence has brought Farfrae to Casterbridge. He,
like Newson, is a stranger.

Hardy favourably describes him as having a 'remarkably
pleasant aspect' (p. 38), and suggests that this young
man is willing to help a complete stranger. There are
similarities between the description of Farfrae and
David (Samuel 17: 12).

Farfrae makes his first contact with Elizabeth-Jane.

GLOSSARY   **yard of clay** a long clay pipe, common at this time

CHAPTER 7

Henchard meets
Farfrae under a
misunderstanding.

Elizabeth-Jane works for the innkeeper to pay for their
keep. The women find that their room adjoins Farfrae's,
and they can overhear a conversation in which Farfrae
tells Henchard his ideas for reclaiming the ruined corn,
and Henchard repeatedly offers him a job as his corn
manager. Farfrae, however, insists he is going to
America.

COMMENT

Henchard hints to Farfrae that there is a dark secret in
his life. It is ironic (see Literary Terms) that Susan
overhears it.

The prim and proper, but resourceful Elizabeth-Jane is
willing to take on demeaning work and to 'sacrifice her
personal comfort and dignity to the common weal' (p. 44).

Hardy's detailed description of Farfrae contrasts starkly with Henchard's, who sees Farfrae as a replica of his own dead brother. This is again to become ironic when later Henchard changes his attitude towards Farfrae.

The third example of irony is that Henchard once gave all he 'owned' to a stranger for five guineas and is now prepared to place all his worldly goods into another stranger's hands.

GLOSSARY   **twelve bushel strength** amount of barley used to make a
              measure of ale
              a quag a muddy piece of ground
              the dog day between 3 July–11 August, Sirius, the dog star,
              rises and sets with the sun. These are thought to be the
              hottest days
              to the pitching until it is empty

CHAPTER 8   Farfrae joins the regular drinkers at The Three
              Mariners and, with some emotion, sings some Scottish
              songs. Everyone is impressed, especially Elizabeth-Jane,
              who feels an affinity with some of the sentiments
              Farfrae displays.

              Meanwhile, outside, Henchard stands and hears the
              music and watches the scene.

COMMENT   Again we see Farfrae as open and amiable and we are
              predisposed to like him.

Note what this   Hardy deliberately contrasts the scene inside The Three
chapter tells us   Mariners with the formal dinner observed in The
about Farfrae.   King's Arms. He pays attention to detail, contrasting
              the rough cups used in The Three Mariners with the
              glasses used in The King's Arms.

              Farfrae's ability to mix easily is contrasted with
              Henchard's isolation. Henchard is an extremely lonely
              and pathetic figure at this point.

A FAMILY REUNETED

GLOSSARY

dying fall a sound dying away gradually

lammigers lame folk

bruckle rough and untrustworthy

chine the rim of a beer barrel

gaberlunzie strolling beggar

staddles wide floor supports which discourages the movement of rats

Flemish ladders ladders which become narrower towards the top

CHAPTER 9

Compare the description of Casterbridge with that in Chapter 4.

The following morning Elizabeth-Jane is sent with a note from her mother to Henchard. Hardy describes her walk through the streets of Casterbridge in a wealth of visual detail. When she arrives at Henchard's yard, she is surprised to find Farfrae there.

Henchard had walked with Farfrae to the Bristol Road and had eventually persuaded him to stay in Casterbridge as his manager. He insists on giving Farfrae an enormous breakfast.

COMMENT

Henchard has achieved his objective: 'Now you are my friend' (p. 65) by securing Farfrae as his manager. Henchard displays a warmth and confidence which is dramatically contrasted later in the novel.

Hardy cleverly advances the plot by using the three characters all moving through crowded Casterbridge.

We are reminded of Henchard's prosperity with the references to his carts in Casterbridge.

GLOSSARY

bloody warriors wallflowers

chassez-déchassez a French dance

Cranstaun's Goblin Page in Walter Scott's *Lay of the last Minstrel* there is an elf who plays practical jokes

CHAPTER 10

Think why he should send her this amount.

Henchard dismisses Jopp, who had unfortunately presumed he would be the manager. This happens just before Elizabeth-Jane enters the office. Henchard gives a warm welcome to Elizabeth-Jane, reads the note from her mother, and writes one to be returned. He also gives her five guineas.

In the note Henchard says he has discovered Elizabeth-Jane is in ignorance. He asks Susan to meet him on the Budmouth Road at the Ring.

COMMENT

Henchard's character is demonstrated dramatically here. His sharp treatment of Joshua Jopp gives an idea of his impetuous nature; he could not be described as indecisive.

This contrasts with his gentlemanly behaviour towards Elizabeth-Jane. He is gentle and considerate, able to assess the situation quickly.

He sends five guineas to Susan as a secret message of remorse, perhaps superstitiously believing that giving her the same amount he sold her for will make matters right.

Henchard does have doubts as to whether Elizabeth-Jane is his. Again, later events will ironically (see Literary Terms) prove him right.

GLOSSARY

the quicker ... Bethesda refers to a pool in Jerusalem, said to heal the first person who entered the water after the angels (John 5: 2–7). Implies he was always the one to be healed

rouge-et-noir his healthy-looking complexion and his black hair

the Ring a Roman amphitheatre, which had high banks to conceal anyone who met inside

CHAPTER 11

The Ring's 'dismal privacy' seems fitting for the reunion.

The detailed description of the Roman amphitheatre sets a background of cruelty for the meeting between Susan and Henchard.

Henchard formulates a plan whereby Susan and Elizabeth-Jane take a cottage in Casterbridge. Henchard will visit them there and remarry Susan. He is concerned that Elizabeth-Jane should not find out the true circumstances of their relationship.

COMMENT

Susan declares her intention to renew the relationship because she is concerned for the welfare of Elizabeth-Jane. She is prepared 'for herself' to go away without any further trouble to him.

As the couple part we are left in doubt as to the sentiments involved. It is still unclear whether there is any love left between them.

GLOSSARY

Jötuns mythological giants in Scandinavian folklore

the sanguine nature of the games refers to gladiatorial fights to the death

Aeolian Aeolus was ruler of the winds

CHAPTER 12

Think about Henchard's motives for telling Farfrae about his past.

When Henchard returns home he finds Farfrae trying to put his books in order. He invites Farfrae to eat with him and afterwards tells Farfrae about his marriage to Susan. Henchard tells Farfrae that he had separated from her and that he now plans to become reunited. He does not tell Farfrae that he sold his wife, but he does tell him that since the time of his separation he has become involved with a woman who lives in Jersey and has also promised to marry her. He entreats Farfrae to help him draft a letter to Jersey breaking off his engagement. He also includes a cheque with the letter.

COMMENT   Farfrae's efficient business sense, his organised and forward thinking contrast with Henchard's rule-of-thumb style and inadequacy with paperwork.

It is plausible that Henchard should confide in Farfrae: his problems were pressing. Farfrae, a relative stranger, is a good listener.

Henchard decides it is better to pay court to Susan so as to keep their 'child's respect' (p. 82): Later, ironically (see Literary Terms), this respect is lost because he has not owned up to the truth.

GLOSSARY   **Achilles** Greek hero who was educated as a hunter and fighter
Laocoöns a priest in Greek legend who was crushed to death by serpents
Job ... birth 'let the day perish when I was born' (Job 3: 3), revealing the dark sad side to Henchard

A *Identify the speaker.*

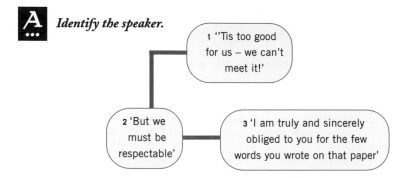

1 "'Tis too good for us – we can't meet it!'

2 'But we must be respectable'

3 'I am truly and sincerely obliged to you for the few words you wrote on that paper'

Identify the person 'to whom' this comment refers.

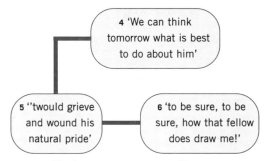

4 'We can think tomorrow what is best to do about him'

5 "'twould grieve and wound his natural pride'

6 'to be sure, to be sure, how that fellow does draw me!'

Check your answers on page 87.

B *Consider these issues.*

a The purpose which the scene in The Three Mariners plays.

b The reason why Hardy describes the Ring very carefully.

c If you can tell from Susan's reactions and relationship with Henchard, whether or not she has forgiven him.

d How Elizabeth-Jane's personality is portrayed in the first twelve chapters.

CHAPTER 13

Note Hardy's use of minor characters here.

Henchard hires a cottage for Susan and Elizabeth-Jane. He visits them frequently, renewing the relationship, and two months later the couple marry.

COMMENT

Henchard is acting purely out of duty. The only love which develops is that of Henchard for Elizabeth-Jane.

Henchard is in some way using his marriage as a means of punishing himself for his wrong-doing.

This sadness is evident even in the description of Susan's cottage.

GLOSSARY

twanking   complaining or grumbling
pair of jumps   a woman's bodice or vest
night raid   a night dress

CHAPTER 14

Notice how Hardy develops the character of Elizabeth-Jane here.

Susan and Elizabeth-Jane settle down to live in their newfound prosperity. Elizabeth-Jane does not spend money or choose expensive or fashionable clothes. Henchard wishes Elizabeth-Jane to become his 'legal' daughter by adoption but Susan secretly passes on her objection to this idea to her daughter. Henchard continues to rely on Farfrae and their relationship grows. At home Henchard demonstrates polite attention but there is little evidence of real love. Elizabeth-Jane and Farfrae find themselves in a granary, the obvious victims of a practical joke.

COMMENT

Elizabeth-Jane emerges as a sensible and beautiful young woman who starts to have a major influence on the other characters. Her mother's health is fading and her concern is genuine and sincere.

A MARRIAGE, A DEATH AND ANOTHER REUNION

Henchard's inability to pay Elizabeth-Jane a compliment on her appearance is contrasted with Farfrae's charming compliments. Henchard's brusqueness is also contrasted with Farfrae's gentle actions, shown when he blows the chaff from Elizabeth-Jane's skirt.

Henchard shows 'tigerish affection' (p. 93) for Farfrae as their relationship grows.

GLOSSARY   **Martinmas Summer** a feast held on 11 November
coulter the cutter in front of the plough
spencer a close fitting bodice
victorine a furry collar worn around the neck

CHAPTER 15

Note what this incident tells about both Henchard and Farfrae.

Henchard and Farfrae clash. Henchard orders Abel Whittle, one of his workmen, to continue with his work without his trousers as a punishment for oversleeping. Farfrae overrides Henchard's orders and makes Henchard look harsh and thoughtless in front of his workmen. Henchard later discovers, from a small child, that Farfrae is gaining in popularity in Casterbridge because he is respected as a good manager and a fair boss.

COMMENT   Elizabeth-Jane's good dress sense, simplicity of manner and sense of humility make her a popular addition to the community.

A relationship between Elizabeth-Jane and Farfrae is beginning to develop, as a counterpoint to the beginning of the end of the relationship between Henchard and Farfrae over the Whittle affair.

Henchard, although still having genuine regard for Farfrae's forthright and honest personality, begins to feel unease over the relationship. This has been precipitated by the conversation with the child. As Hardy cleverly puts it: 'the seed that was to lift the foundation of this friendship'.

y

GLOSSARY   **the prophet ... go gay** 'And taking gold, as it were for a virgin that loveth to go gay, they make crowns for the heads of their gods' (The Apocrypha, Baruch 6: 8)

Rochefoucauld philosopher who suggested that self-love is the prime motive of human beings.

fretted my gizzard worried

moment-hand a second hand which moves each time the pendulum swings

scantling scrap

fairing a present

diment a diamond

chap o'wax a good-looking man or one who is becoming successful

CHAPTER 16

Compare the festivities being prepared in this chapter: notice what the festivities tell you about the men who are organising them.

Both Henchard and Farfrae organise celebrations for a national holiday. Farfrae's is under cover and has an admission charge. Henchard's features more traditional country pursuits, is outdoors, but free. The weather changes and most of Casterbridge favour Farfrae's entertainment. Henchard openly remarks that Farfrae is nearing the end of his time as a manager with his firm. Farfrae accepts this and decides to move on.

COMMENT

Hardy uses fate, in the form of a change in the weather, to make a turn in the relationship between Henchard and Farfrae.

Hardy lets us see another side to Henchard's character, for he is now courteous to Farfrae in a rather formal way. Henchard's mood has swung completely. Instead of smiles there are glares and an obvious resentment for Farfrae's popularity. 'Everyone is full of him' (p. 109).

Henchard was prepared to pay for the entertainment he offered: yet another example of money putting matters right, and perhaps some notion on Henchard's part that this would emphasise his role as 'master'.

A MARRIAGE, A DEATH AND ANOTHER REUNION

GLOSSARY   Correggio (1494–1534) a famous Italian artist

stumpoll a fool

by a chaw by a mouthful

randy merrymaking

top sawyer when two men cut wood the one who was above
remained clean; the other got covered in sawdust

CHAPTER 17

Compare the   At the end of the evening Farfrae walks Elizabeth-Jane
attitudes of Farfrae home and almost proposes to her. Farfrae sets up
and Henchard   business on his own. At first he avoids direct
towards each other.   competition with Henchard, but as his business
develops this gets to be impossible and he becomes a
rival to Henchard. Henchard is furious and forbids
Elizabeth-Jane to see Farfrae and writes to Farfrae
forbidding him to see Elizabeth-Jane.

COMMENT   Elizabeth-Jane has realised she is in love with Farfrae
and knows this is what her mother wants, but the
breach between Farfrae and her father signals the end
of any possible marriage.

Elizabeth-Jane spends many lonely hours pretending
that all is well by dressing up and looking in the mirror,
'just enough to make him silly, and not enough to keep
him so' (p. 115). Ironically (see Literary Terms) just at a
time when her inhibitions are falling away she must
face disappointment in her love for Farfrae.

Henchard finds his support by townspeople fading
away. Hardy cleverly emphasises this by using
Bellerophon – a mythical hero who once deserted by
gods and good fortune was left to walk alone facing all
kinds of hazardous tasks.

Farfrae continues to act honourably: 'I cannot hurt the
trade of a man who's been so kind to me' (p. 117).

GLOSSARY   **Jacob in Padan-Aram** all Jacob received as payment for his work were the ring-straked and spotted cattle, but after this all these cattle did well and prospered (Genesis 30: 24–4)
Novalis a German author
Faust a character who was supposed to have sold his soul to the devil

CHAPTER 18

Note what Lucetta's letter tells you of her past and future plans.

Henchard receives a letter from Lucetta, the young woman in Jersey, in which she asks him to return all her letters to her when she passes through Casterbridge. Henchard goes to the arranged appointment but Lucetta fails to show. Meanwhile Susan is writing a note to Henchard. She asks that the letter will not be opened until the day of Elizabeth-Jane's marriage. Susan confesses to having written the notes which brought Farfrae and Elizabeth-Jane together at Durnover Barton. She had hoped that they would eventually marry.

COMMENT   In yet another twist of fate, as Susan lies dying Lucetta re-enters Henchard's life.

It could be said that Lucetta returns from a regretted past just as Susan and Elizabeth-Jane had done, and once again Henchard may feel he has to do the 'right' thing.

Letters play an important part in this chapter.

Susan's letters will be opened at the wrong time, so will the letters written by Lucetta, both with tragic (see Literary Terms) consequences.

Susan's death again reminds us of the superstition and ritual endemic at this time. Susan's request that four pennies be used to weigh down her eyes after her death is acknowledged by the rustics. Hardy cleverly uses these to show the true qualities of human nature: 'Why should death rob life o' fourpence? ... I say there was no treason in it' (p. 123).

A MARRIAGE, A DEATH AND ANOTHER REUNION

GLOSSARY   **ounce pennies** minted for special occasions, much heavier

                     doxology a mistake, he meant theology

CHAPTER 19

Directing all his attention to Elizabeth-Jane after Susan's death, Henchard decides to tell her the story of his separation from Susan all those years before and that she is his daughter. However, fate again plays a cruel hand, as Henchard searches for proof of his story he comes across Susan's letter with a damaged seal. He cannot resist the temptation to read it. The letter discloses that Elizabeth-Jane is Newson's daughter, born a year after her separation from Henchard, their own baby having died the year before. Henchard decides not to tell Elizabeth-Jane as she has accepted him as her father, but it does change the way in which Henchard deals with her.

COMMENT

The timing of this discovery is really cruel and affects Henchard dramatically (see Literary Terms). He has just lost Susan; been estranged from Farfrae and now finds that Elizabeth-Jane is not his natural daughter.

Look at the effect that the description of the riverbank has in this chapter.

Hardy emphasises Henchard's loneliness as he describes his walk along the river bank. These sentences are flooded with melodramatic and metaphorical language (see Literary Terms). 'Mournful phases' and 'torturing cramps' and 'voice of desolation' (p. 129) all indicate the deep gloom and despondency to which Henchard will sink.

Henchard now feels after reading Susan's letter that his remarriage had been no more than 'dust and ashes' (p. 131).

GLOSSARY   **the brethren ... Joseph** Joseph said unto his brethren, 'I am Joseph; doth my father yet live?' And his brethren could not answer him: for they were troubled at his presence (Genesis 45: 3)

Prester John   mythical king who tried to capture paradise, and
was punished by the gods

Schwarzwasser   black water

CHAPTER 20

Think about what the incident on page 134 tells us of Elizabeth-Jane's character.

Elizabeth-Jane continues to try and improve herself, but Henchard always finds fault with her and is either merely bad-tempered or aggressive. Yet another letter is despatched to Farfrae. This time Henchard indicates he has no objection to Farfrae seeing his daughter. Obviously he is keen to get rid of Newson's daughter. Elizabeth-Jane is made miserable by Henchard's treatment of her, especially when Henchard finds out that she has worked in The Three Mariners.

Elizabeth-Jane visits her mother's grave and is approached by a lady. They strike up a conversation and the lady invites her to go and live with her as her companion in a house in town which she has just bought.

COMMENT

Hardy builds up the tension here. Henchard's rather volatile and unstable disposition is evidenced in his treatment of Elizabeth-Jane, especially of his reaction to what he sees as her reduced social status.

Elizabeth-Jane's natural sense of humility angers Henchard even more.

The mysterious lady from Jersey is introduced, although not as yet by name.

Henchard has not been reinvited to reapply as alderman but Farfrae has, and this increases the tension between the two men.

Henchard now sees Farfrae as 'a treacherous upstart' (p. 137).

A MARRIAGE, A DEATH AND ANOTHER REUNION

GLOSSARY　　jowned　indeed
　　　　　　　　Minerva　Athena, goddess of wisdom
　　　　　　　　Princess Ida　a character in Tennyson's *The Princess* (1847)
　　　　　　　　chain shot and sandbags　writing which is much coarser
　　　　　　　　Austerlitz　a battle (1805) which marked a turning point in
　　　　　　　　　Napoleon's history
　　　　　　　　leery　exhausted

CHAPTER 21

Think about why At dusk Elizabeth-Jane goes to look at High-Place Hall
Henchard's and where the mysterious lady lives. As Elizabeth-Jane
Elizabeth-Jane's leaves Henchard approaches and enters the house by the
visits to High-Place back door, but Elizabeth-Jane fails to recognise him.
Hall are kept a
secret. Later Henchard is told of Elizabeth-Jane's plans to leave.
He agrees and offers to pay her an annual allowance.

The following day just as Elizabeth-Jane is preparing to
leave, Henchard asks her to stay. He has learned how
much she has tried to improve herself and feels sorry
that he has dealt with her so harshly. When Elizabeth-
Jane tells Henchard her new address he is very shocked.

COMMENT　Again Henchard feels he can rid himself of his moral
obligation by offering money, just as he did with Susan
and Lucetta.

Lucetta's motives in asking Elizabeth-Jane to live with her
are revealed in her agitation with Elizabeth-Jane when
she discovers Elizabeth-Jane has not told her father.

The reader becomes aware that Lucetta's motives are to
attract Henchard to the house.

GLOSSARY　　Palladian　Italian-style architecture
　　　　　　　　tailing　little bits of corn
　　　　　　　　fly　a small carriage
　　　　　　　　passenger　used as 'passer-by'

y

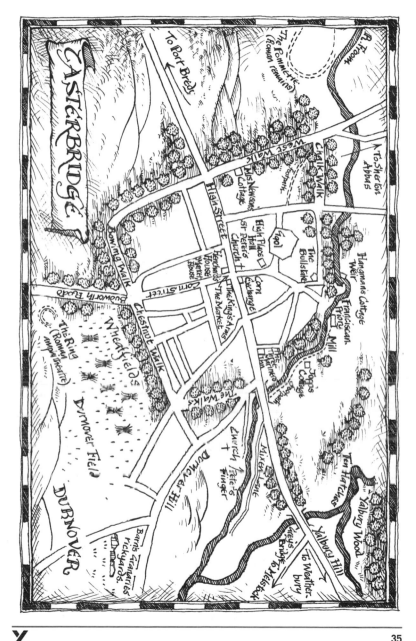

A MARRIAGE, A DEATH AND ANOTHER REUNION

CHAPTER 22

Note how Lucetta's attitude changes toward Elizabeth-Jane in this chapter. Hardy uses a flashback technique (see Literary Terms) to reveal what had happened the night before. Lucetta had written to Henchard telling of an abrupt change in her position. She is now to be called Templeman not Le Sueur. Lucetta suggests marriage to Henchard and asks him to visit her the next day. When Henchard does visit he is put off, and feels indignant at being treated this way. He does not pay Lucetta the compliment of visiting her the following day. Lucetta has learned of the difficulties between Elizabeth-Jane and her father, and has presumed that this is the reason for Henchard's indifference towards her. She decides she must get rid of Elizabeth-Jane. Miss Templeman has a visitor. It is not, however, Henchard.

COMMENT

It is important to see how the letters are used as a device (see Literary Terms) for understanding the motivation of the characters. Lucetta's first letter to the mayor encourages his sense of duty, and as he is lonely he feels inclined to marry her. However, her second letter demonstrates how she is using Elizabeth-Jane.

There is a parallel between Susan and Lucetta in their use of Elizabeth-Jane. Susan, by writing to Henchard and sending the note with Elizabeth-Jane, hoped to secure a house for them both. Lucetta, by employing Elizabeth-Jane, hoped to attract Henchard to visit her home. Again the object of the exercise was marriage.

Henchard again misinterprets the situation and stands apart, appearing moody and obstinate.

GLOSSARY

etourderie thoughtlessness
Titian a famous painter
the weak Apostle said to be Peter (Matthew 26: 73)
Candlemas fair celebrated on 2 February by Catholics
cyma-recta an architectural term meaning that the moulding of a cornice has the concave curve uppermost

Y

A — Identify the speaker.

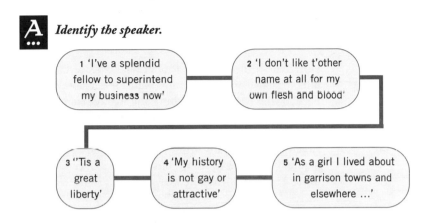

1 'I've a splendid fellow to superintend my business now'

2 'I don't like t'other name at all for my own flesh and blood'

3 "Tis a great liberty'

4 'My history is not gay or attractive'

5 'As a girl I lived about in garrison towns and elsewhere ...'

Identify the person 'to whom' this comment refers.

6 'But daze me if ever I see a man wait so long before to take so little!'

7 'I wonder why she wants to get rid of me today!'

Check your answers on page 87.

B — Consider these issues.

a Note how we see into Henchard's character through the eyes of Elizabeth-Jane.

b Hardy uses the national holiday to contrast the characters of Farfrae and Henchard.

c Farfrae, Lucetta and Henchard all have secrets which complicate the action in varying ways.

d Notice the effect Susan's secret has when it is revealed.

CHAPTER 23

Farfrae has called to see Elizabeth-Jane. Lucetta finds him attractive and asks him to wait for Elizabeth-Jane. Farfrae who has been watching the market from the window decides to employ a young man, who would have had to be separated from his old father and sweetheart. Lucetta is impressed by Farfrae's generous nature. Farfrae leaves to do business and Lucetta refuses to see Henchard when he arrives.

COMMENT   Although Farfrae has come to High-Place Hall to see Elizabeth-Jane it is ironic (see Literary Terms) that he is attracted to Lucetta, as she is to him.

Lucetta fears that her past will be revealed. She entreats Farfrae not to listen to gossip about her, 'If they tell you I'm a coquette, which some may, because of the incidents of my life, don't believe it, for I am not' (p. 167).

Again the reader sees another auction. The 'hiring fair' could have meant the separation of a young man from his sweetheart had it not been for Farfrae 'quite brimming with sentiment' (p. 167).

Lucetta tends to use Elizabeth-Jane for her own purpose.

Lucetta's attitude towards Elizabeth-Jane changes yet again, as she sees in her a possible 'watch-dog to keep her father off' (p. 168).

GLOSSARY   **hyperborean** belonging to the north

kerseymere fine wool

wagon-tilts canvas covering of wagons

Lady-day 25 March, a ceremony for the Annunciation to the Virgin Mary

CHAPTER 24

Look how character
is revealed through
the various
reactions to the
horse-drill.

From Lucetta's window both women look out eagerly each Saturday for a glimpse of Farfrae. When Farfrae introduces a new seed-drill to Casterbridge the women go down to the market place to take a look. Elizabeth-Jane senses the attraction between Lucetta and Farfrae. Henchard derides the seed-drill.

Some days later Lucetta tells Elizabeth-Jane the story of a woman who was promised in a love match to one man but has since become attracted to another. Although Lucetta makes the case sound hypothetical and abstract, Elizabeth-Jane guesses she is talking about herself.

COMMENT

The dresses are a
clever device (see
Literary Terms).

Hardy cleverly sets the time of the novel by having the 'horse-drill', at just before the repeal of the Corn Laws.

Hardy also indicates that Casterbridge is a small provincial town, lacking in fashion. This is why Lucetta's dresses arrive from London. We are aware that Lucetta, capable of duplicity, is no more than the clothes she wears (p. 170).

Dazzling in her finery Lucetta is now seeing Farfrae as her own.

The chapter finishes with Lucetta's confidence to Elizabeth-Jane who will not give an opinion on the problem.

GLOSSARY

the Heptarchy Saxon England
some falls by the wayside ... among thorns from the parable of the sower (Matthew 13: 3–9)
'He that observeth ... shall not sow' Ecclesiastes 11: 4
rencounter casual meeting, from French *rencontre*

A SECRET MARRIAGE

CHAPTER 25

When Farfrae calls on Lucetta he ignores Elizabeth-Jane, as does Henchard. Elizabeth-Jane quickly accepts both men's indifference to her. Henchard proposes marriage to Lucetta, but her response is evasive.

COMMENT

Henchard, single-minded in his pursuit of Lucetta, regards her 'as almost his property', a phrase intended to remind us of the auction.

Decide which character gains the reader's sympathy here.

We have sympathy for Henchard: his lack of gentle manners and ignorance of fashion are highlighted when he appears in Lucetta's drawing room.

Elizabeth-Jane is ignored by Henchard, Farfrae and Lucetta.

GLOSSARY

protean variety Proteus was able to change his shape at will (Greek myth)

'meaner beauties of the night' stars

CHAPTER 26

Henchard hires Jopp as his manager and directs him to 'cut out' Farfrae. Jopp is keen to take revenge on Farfrae whom he sees as having lost him the job to begin with. Henchard visits Fall, the weather prophet who says that August will be a bad month. Henchard buys up grain hoping that the prices will be higher later, but August is a good month and the prices fall. Henchard has to sell corn at a loss in order to pay his bills, and worse than this Henchard is forced to borrow money from the bank. Jopp is sacked and leaves vowing to take revenge.

COMMENT

Hardy uses the symbol (see Literary Terms) of Henchard and Farfrae vying for the bread and butter in Lucetta's drawing room – almost a religious scenario. This contrasts with the superstitious visit of Henchard to Fall.

Rivalry in business has now turned to rivalry in love. Think of possible effects it may have.

Here, each is aware that the other is also a suitor to Lucetta. Note how Henchard listens to Farfrae knocking at Lucetta's door and thinks it is 'somebody between gentle and simple'.

Only Elizabeth Jane is able to see things as they really are: she exclaims 'How ridiculous of all three of them!' (p. 186).

Poor Jopp, having lost his job to Farfrae to begin with, loses it a second time because of Farfrae's success. We are to see later that it is Jopp who brings down Lucetta; it is he who discloses the secrets in her letters.

Jopp hates both Farfrae and Henchard.

GLOSSARY

refluent flowing back

pis aller last resource

immediately before … made in grain the Corn Laws, imposing a heavy tax on foreign corn to protect the English farmers, were repealed in 1846

Alastor an avenging god

the evil scrofula, a disease which enlarges the lymphatic glands

dung mixen a dung hill or manure heap

living in Revelations when the four angels blew trumpets heralding the end of the world (Revelations 8: 7–12)

like the pale

CHAPTER 27

How many other 'secrets' of Lucetta's wait to be told?

Just as the harvest begins fate takes a hand and the weather worsens. Henchard delays selling his corn and loses large amounts of money. Henchard follows Lucetta to her meeting with Farfrae and overhears some of their conversation. He returns quickly to Lucetta's house, arriving before her, and makes her promise to marry him using Elizabeth-Jane as witness. Elizabeth-Jane is bewildered by her father's apparent power over Lucetta.

A SECRET MARRIAGE

COMMENT   Henchard earns our sympathy over his loss over the
           corn and Lucetta's duplicity, but it does not extend to
           his cave-man approach to marriage. The scene in
           Lucetta's drawing room tells us much about Henchard's
           character.

           The way in which the rival waggoners fight over
           Henchard's upset load of hay is parodied (see Literary
           Terms) later with the fight between Farfrae and
           Henchard and Henchard losing everything.

           We see further evidence of Henchard's
           superstitiousness: 'I wonder if it can be that somebody
           has been roasting a waxen image of me, or stirring an
           unholy brew to confound me' (p. 195).

GLOSSARY   **wailing** swaying, wandering

           gawk-hammer awkward, stupid

           thill a horse between shafts

           giddying-worm infests sheep, making them first giddy, then
            killing them

           shocks piles of sheaves of corn

           lucubrations night-time study

           no'thern not making sense

CHAPTER 28

Think whether   The next day Henchard is standing in as a magistrate.
Henchard's fairness The furmity woman had been accused of being a public
extends to those   nuisance. She recognises Henchard and reveals to the
closer to him.   whole assembly his secret. Henchard makes no attempt
                     to conceal the truth or to deny the accusation. This is
                     the beginning of Henchard's social and financial
                     decline. News spreads quickly and upsets Lucetta, who
                     decides to go away to Port Bredy for a few days. It is
                     clear to us at this point that Lucetta does not want to
                     marry Henchard. Henchard looks for her and goes to
                     meet her on the Port Bredy road.

COMMENT   The courtroom scene is one of humour, albeit sardonic and satirical (see Literary Terms), beginning with Stubberd's comically delivered evidence, through to the furmity woman's obvious ease with courtroom procedures and practices.

Henchard could have denied the accusation but, to his credit, he did not.

Again, we see the peculiar mixture which makes up Henchard's character: integrity and forthrightness.

GLOSSARY   **ashlar** a building constructed of stone which has been built to a regular shape

clouds drop fatness from Psalm 65: 11

instinct, Hannah Dominy instant, *anno domini*

turmit-head a blockhead or thick head

larry a fuss or commotion

CHAPTER *29*

Lucetta, who has walked along the Port Bredy road, in the expectation of meeting someone approaching Casterbridge, meets Elizabeth-Jane. The women are chased by a bull and find themselves penned in an old barn. Henchard manages to seize and tether the bull and save both their lives. Henchard takes Lucetta home and after asking her to secure a loan for him, is told that she is already married to Farfrae.

COMMENT   Lucetta is very restless, rather like a pacing animal, as she walks back towards Port Bredy. The reader suspects that she will be meeting Farfrae but at this point it is no more than a hint.

Hardy portrays Henchard in two starkly contrasting ways. His physical aggression with the bull is contrasted with his courteousness and gentleness with the women.

Y

A SECRET MARRIAGE

Think whether the reasons Lucetta gives Henchard for marrying Farfrae are justified.

Henchard is brave and selfless here and we are inclined to feel sorry for him as we guess Lucetta's secret before Henchard is told.

Henchard's relationship with Lucetta somewhat parallels his relationship with Susan. He tries to make money by using both these relationships, and ironically (see Literary Terms) loses the relationship in the end.

GLOSSARY   **Abrahamic success** a biblical reference: Genesis 13: 2
Yahoo beasts in *Gulliver's Travels*, with human shape and animal vices
the Thames … yore a tunnel under the Thames, opened in 1843
Gurth's collar of brass in Walter Scott's *Ivanhoe*, the pigman had a brass collar on his neck

CHAPTER 30

Think whether Elizabeth-Jane could have stayed in the same house after this treatment.

Elizabeth-Jane is angry and confused by Lucetta's news of her marriage. She feels that Lucetta has acted dishonourably, and moves out to find some lodgings of her own in the street where Henchard lives. Farfrae prepares to move into High-Place Hall.

COMMENT   Lucetta is completely ignorant of Elizabeth-Jane and Farfrae's earlier affections and so is unable to understand Farfrae and Elizabeth-Jane's reactions.

The theme of deviance continues, because Lucetta has married Farfrae without telling him of her past.

Lucetta does not show any concern for Elizabeth-Jane's welfare. She accepts Elizabeth-Jane's departure from her house with indifference.

Lucetta is consumed with her own affairs.

Y

GLOSSARY   **John Gilpin** a 'linen draper bold' in Cowper's poem, who embarks on a long ride

Ovid this quotation means 'I see the better things and approve of them: I follow the worst'

Nathan tones Nathan condemned David for his marriage to Bathsheba (2 Samuel 12: 1–9)

CHAPTER 31

Look at Abel Whittle here, and how life has changed in the corn stores.

With the story of his selling his wife common gossip, Henchard's reputation is now completely destroyed as he is declared a bankrupt. Although he again shows himself honourable, in the ways in which he deals with his creditors, his business still suffers and a downward spiral continues. Henchard is forced to leave his splendid home and ironically (see Literary Terms) take up meagre lodgings with Jopp. Elizabeth-Jane is unable to see him as Henchard gives strict orders that he is not to be visited.

COMMENT

The original auction of all that Henchard possessed – his wife and child – is repeated a second time. This time Henchard loses everything – peace of mind, respect and dignity – all over again.

GLOSSARY   **vitrified** blue glazed bricks laid in a pattern

arch-labels mouldings over doors, window etc.

cat-head beam hanging over a wall, to which a pulley is attached

CHAPTER 32

Compare this meeting with their first.

On a notorious bridge to the east of Casterbridge Henchard meets Jopp who tells him with some delight that Farfrae has bought all his possessions including his house. The next to meet Henchard on the bridge is Farfrae who offers him a room in his old house. Farfrae's intention of giving Henchard his furniture is refused, but at this point Henchard seems to realise that he may have misjudged Farfrae. Henchard becomes ill, and eventually Elizabeth-Jane is allowed access to him and offers to nurse him.

COMMENT   Farfrae displays a puzzling persona (see Literary Terms)
here. We know that he is a tough businessman, paying
less than Henchard and expecting harder work, but now
he shows kindness towards Henchard.

Elizabeth-Jane gives Henchard hope for the future, and
is the only thing of any value left in Henchard's life.

GLOSSARY   **Adonis** Venus loved a handsome youth called Adonis
journeywork work paid for by the day
the Prophet's chamber chamber of Elisha (2 Kings 4: 8–11)
stock a wide collar which acted as both collar and tie

CHAPTER 33

Forty people have met after church in The Three
Mariners for a customary drink, and Henchard chooses
this moment to proclaim an end to his twenty-one
years of abstinence. He asks the church choir to
accompany him with the doom-laden Psalm 109. The
choir refuses to sing it but Henchard insists, and it
becomes obvious that the threatening psalm was
intended for Farfrae and Lucetta to hear as they stroll
by the window. Elizabeth-Jane enters and saves the
situation by taking Henchard home.

*Compare the scene
of Henchard
singing with the
earlier scene of
Farfrae
entertaining the
assembly.*

Elizabeth-Jane goes to help her father in Farfrae's yard,
after Henchard has objected to Abel Whittle's 'pitying
eyes upon him'. Lucetta comes upon Henchard there,
and he is witheringly sarcastic to her. Next day she
writes him a letter begging him not to treat her so
bitterly. Henchard, realising he could show this letter to
Farfrae and compromise Lucetta, nonetheless burns it.

Elizabeth, taking Henchard tea in the yard, sees him
almost tempted to push Farfrae through a trap door,
though resisting it. She determines to warn Farfrae of
her stepfather's dangerous state of mind.

COMMENT   Hardy's description of the ring of drinkers with
their mugs, and their resemblance to a stone circle,

THE DOWNFALL OF MICHAEL HENCHARD

CHAPTER 35

Lucetta's anxiety increases when she overhears an exchange between Farfrae and Henchard. However, when Farfrae goes up to Lucetta she realises that Henchard has not revealed her identity. Next day she sends Henchard a note asking for her letters back and arranges to meet him that evening at the Ring.

Note how Henchard's meeting with Susan at the Ring compares with his meeting with Lucetta.

Henchard faced with the quietly dressed and subdued Lucetta at the Ring is reminded of his previous meeting there with Susan. He promises to return Lucetta's letters the following day.

GLOSSARY   toilette a woman's preparation of herself to face the world, her dress, hair, complexion, etc

COMMENT   First Henchard is portrayed as villainous and evil as he reads her letters to Farfrae. Here he is gentle and empathetic to Lucetta.

Lucetta is the driving-force in the chapter.

Lucetta is portrayed as passionate, honest and highly strung; motivated to protect her newfound happiness with Farfrae.

Lucetta cannot bring herself to confess to Farfrae. She feels he will see her previous relationship with Henchard as 'her fault' (p. 255) and she fears rejection.

CHAPTER 36

Jopp waylays Lucetta and asks her to recommend him to Farfrae for the post of manager, but Lucetta, anxious to catch Farfrae, is rude and dismissive.

Later Jopp is asked by Henchard to take the letters back to Lucetta. However, on the way he meets friends and they all go for a drink at Peter's Finger inn. There he opens the letters and reads them to the assembled group. Nance Mockridge suggests the skimmington-ride.

ritualises Henchard's end to his twenty-one years of abstinence.

Hardy's use of the words of Psalm 109 adds considerable power to Henchard's bitter feelings about Farfrae and Lucetta.

On two occasions Henchard is offered an opportunity to wreak revenge on Farfrae:

- when he receives Lucetta's letter
- when he is standing tantalisingly close to Farfrae and the trap door

but Henchard's sense of decency always outweighs his anger.

Ironically (see Literary Terms), despite Henchard's loathing of Whittle's pitying concern, it will be Whittle who will stand by him to the end.

Henchard is doubly humiliated by having to work for Farfrae in what was once his own business, now that Farfrae has married Lucetta.

GLOSSARY   rantipole rubbish wild and rough
as lief just as well
Rosalind's explanation Rosalind is a character from Shakespeare's *As You Like It*. The quote 'mistress know yourself! down on your knees … ' is from this play

A *Identify the speaker.*

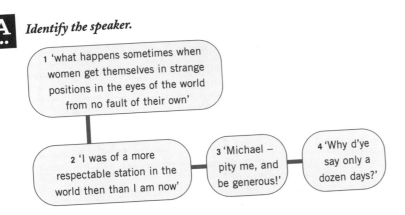

1 'what happens sometimes when women get themselves in strange positions in the eyes of the world from no fault of their own'

2 'I was of a more respectable station in the world then than I am now'

3 'Michael – pity me, and be generous!'

4 'Why d'ye say only a dozen days?'

Identify the person 'to whom' this comment refers.

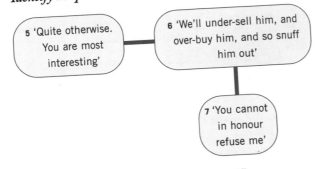

5 'Quite otherwise. You are most interesting'

6 'We'll under-sell him, and over-buy him, and so snuff him out'

7 'You cannot in honour refuse me'

Check your answers on page 87.

B *Consider these issues.*

a Lucetta's character is further revealed. Make notes on any evidence you find to support your ideas about her.

b Plot Henchard through Chapters 23 to 33. Note what the major reasons are for the changes.

c Think about the part the 'bull' scene plays.

d Think about the kind of relationship there is between Farfrae and Lucetta and what affect Henchard's presence would have been in the house.

CHAPTER 34

Elizabeth-Jane goes to warn Farfrae of a possible danger from Henchard.

Consider Farfrae's remark: 'what harm have I done him that he should try to wrong me?' (p. 245).

Farfrae pretends to make light of this but is later told by the town clerk that Henchard hates him. Farfrae had planned to set Henchard up in a seed-shop business; now, despite his genuine regard for Henchard's well-being, he decides to postpone the venture.

Lucetta meets Henchard in the market and asks him to return her letters. Henchard remembers they are in the safe, in what is now Farfrae's home. He decides to read the letters to Farfrae but, after reading some of them aloud, fails to disclose their writer.

COMMENT

Farfrae speaks to Elizabeth-Jane with 'the cheeriness of a superior' (p. 244) – perhaps an indication of his conveniently short memory.

He does not take her warning seriously at first, but later reflects on what she has said.

Lucetta fears for Farfrae and wants him to leave Casterbridge.

Fate takes a hand when the mayor dies, and Farfrae is made mayor. Farfrae now becomes everything that Henchard was.

Notice Hardy's use of Lucetta's letters to increase tension and simultaneously add a touch of humour.

Farfrae seems to listen with polite interest whilst Henchard builds up to revealing Lucetta's name, but ultimately cannot bring himself to do so.

GLOSSARY

siller shoon silver shoes
Tamerlane's trumpet Tamburlaine (1330–1400) was a great Tartar conqueror who was said to have used huge trumpets
Aphrodite Greek goddess of love

Compare the   Meanwhile a stranger has entered Casterbridge and
description of the   contributes a sovereign towards the skimmington-ride.
sailor in Ch. 1 and Jopp carries on to deliver the letters and a grateful and
the stranger here.   relieved Lucetta burns them.

COMMENT   Jopp seems to be used as a device for trouble. He has
                mentioned Jersey to both Henchard and Lucetta, and
                we become aware of the possible threat he may be.

                Ironically (see Literary Terms), like Susan's letter, the
                letters from Henchard are not sealed properly; this
                almost removes the question of blame from the
                inappropriate readers.

                Here Hardy returns to portray the lower classes of
                Casterbridge, giving a clear picture of life in Mixen
                Lane and a feeling of the changing face of rural
                England.

                Hardy uses the furmity woman for the last time here, to
                ask Jopp what his parcel contains.

GLOSSARY   Adullam a refuge mentioned in the Bible (1 Samuel 22: 1–2)
                Ashton-Ravenswood In *The Bride of Lammermoor* by Sir Walter
                  Scott, Ravenswood, about to fight a duel, just disappears
                swingels cudgels, a weapon
                oven-pyle long-handled wooden shovel for putting bread into
                  the oven

CHAPTER 37

                Henchard asks if he may join the welcoming party which
                is about to meet a member of the royal family as he
                passes through Casterbridge. His request is refused,
                because he is no longer a member of the council. He
                decides to prepare his own welcome and just as the royal
                personage alights, steps forward in shabby clothes waving
                a home-made Union Jack. Farfrae roughly orders him

away. Plans for the skimmington-ride are well underway, which will take place that night. Two men, Solomon Longways and Christopher Coney, feel rather sorry and decide to send a note 'to those most concerned' (p. 274) to warn them of the events of the night.

COMMENT

Note how Farfrae has changed from his description in Chapter 6.

Farfrae's smart, official appearance is highlighted by Henchard's poor and shabby clothes he had once worn as mayor, now 'weather-beaten garments of bygone years' (p. 271).

Ironically (see Literary Terms), there are two rides parodied (see Literary Terms) here. The wealth of Casterbridge concentrate on the ride of the royal through the town, and much spiteful, vicious talk takes place behind hands by the wealthy womenfolk; some of it overheard by Lucetta. Whereas the poorer folk have their attention focused on the skimmington-ride and talk just as maliciously but in a more open and honest way.

GLOSSARY

fête carillonnée a festival marked by a peal of bells

Pharaoh's chariots Moses and the Israelites were pursued by the Egyptians (Exodus 14: 25)

hontish proud

toppered toppled down

put fitting

CHAPTER 38

Henchard says 'no man ever loved another as I did thee'. Can this be true?.

Henchard, rebuffed, goes to hide behind the ladies' stand. He overhears Lucetta deny that he had ever helped Farfrae. Henchard is livid and vows to take revenge. He asks Farfrae to meet him at the corn stores. Henchard dramatically ties up one arm and forces Farfrae into a fight, which because he is a much stronger man, he wins. High above the ground Henchard has Farfrae in a situation where he could kill him, but he collapses to the ground and lets Farfrae go.

Y

Farfrae is shaken but continues to keep an appointment at Weatherbury.

Henchard again finds himself on the bridge. He has decided to wait for Farfrae's return to beg his forgiveness. On the bridge he hears noise from the town but does not understand what is happening.

COMMENT   Hardy completes the downfall of Henchard here. We see a desperate man, viciously waiting to kill Farfrae but still compassionate enough to bind his right arm, so as not to have an unfair advantage.

Farfrae seems willing to humour Henchard, even to trust him. Farfrae remains kindly disposed towards Henchard as he always has.

Henchard's victory is short-lived, as he immediately regrets what he has done, and seems shocked at the depths to which he has sunk.

GLOSSARY   *Weltlust* worldly pleasure

CHAPTER 39

Farfrae is obviously popular with his men.

Farfrae who had prepared to go to Budmouth, has received an anonymous note asking him to go to Weatherbury, in exactly the opposite direction. This note has been sent by some of Farfrae's employees to keep him out of the route of the skimmington-ride. Henchard happens to overhear Farfrae tell Whittle of the change of direction.

Elizabeth-Jane displays several examples of her consideration here.

Lucetta, who is waiting for Farfrae to come home, is drawn to the window by the maids. Elizabeth-Jane seems to try to stop Lucetta seeing the skimmington-ride, but Lucetta insists on staying at the window to watch the scene and quickly interprets the events and realises who the effigies are supposed to represent by the clothes the dummies are wearing. She has a massive epileptic fit. The doctor is sent for. He pronounces Lucetta's condition as serious and sends a servant to find Farfrae.

Meanwhile one of the magistrates attempts to stop the procession but is too late.

COMMENT

It is ironic (see Literary Terms) that Lucetta for the first time in many months feels secure. She is married to the man she loves, and has burned the incriminating letters, and yet it is exactly at this time that her secret is revealed.

Once again Elizabeth-Jane is at hand at a time of great disruption and calmly tries to stop Lucetta going to the window.

Hardy lightens the end of this chapter by introducing the two comic constables, Dogberry and Verges, humorously depicting their total ineffectuality.

GLOSSARY

the malter's chimbley a chimney which obstructs the view
crouds fiddles
skimmington-ride where lifesized effigies are used to represent people who have committed adultery
humstrums hurdy-gurdies
serpents wind instruments

felo de se suicide

the crew of Comus Comus, god of mirth, who had magical
powers and was accompanied by a crew of noisy revellers

C<small>HAPTER</small> 40

See how many
examples of fate
there are in this
chapter.

Henchard sees the end of the skimmington-ride and
goes to find Elizabeth-Jane who is at Farfrae's house.
Here he learns of Lucetta's fit and dangerous state of
health. Henchard tells them that Farfrae has gone to
Weatherbury, but he is ignored. Feeling frustration he
goes off to look for Farfrae himself.

Farfrae does not trust Henchard and refuses to believe
the truth, interpreting it as a trap. Despite Henchard's
pleas Farfrae refuses to travel to Casterbridge
immediately; he returns via Mellstock over two hours
later, to spend the last hours with Lucetta.

Jopp tells Henchard that a sea-captain has been looking
for him. Henchard has a restless night concerned not
only for Lucetta, but also Elizabeth-Jane and Farfrae.
At daybreak Henchard hears that Lucetta has died.

C<small>OMMENT</small>

Note Hardy's change of style for Lucetta's death. It is
almost skimmed over, with hints of how much she tells
Farfrae of her relationship with Henchard.

Hardy notifies Casterbridge of Lucetta's death by
simply removing the muffler from the door knocker.

Henchard is, ironically (see Literary Terms), neither
believed or trusted. He is portrayed as a pitiful figure
here and we can only feel sorry for him as he walks and
runs, argues and pleads for Farfrae to return to Lucetta.

Henchard has now sunk as low as he can. He finds comfort
with Elizabeth-Jane and vows to love her as his own.

Again Jopp is used as a portender of bad news. It is he
who tells Henchard that a sea-captain has called.

THE DOWNFALL OF MICHAEL HENCHARD

GLOSSARY　　　a less scrupulous Job Job 3: 1–16
　　　　　　　　Lucifer the morning star

CHAPTER 41

Elizabeth-Jane goes to visit her 'father'. She is so tired she falls asleep while he cooks breakfast. Newson calls but Henchard tells the sailor that Susan and her daughter are dead. Newson is very upset and leaves Casterbridge.

'The sense of supernatural was strong in this unhappy man' (p. 304): think where else we see this.

Henchard again regrets he has not told the truth and fears that he will be found out and that Newson will return. Henchard goes to the weir to drown himself, but there in the water is an effigy of himself. Being superstitious he takes this as an omen that he should not drown himself and goes home. Elizabeth-Jane is alarmed and concerned for Henchard and offers to live with him again.

COMMENT

Henchard deceives again: 'mad lies like a child in pure mockery of consequences' (p. 300), this time through fear of losing Elizabeth-Jane.

This is parodied (see Literary Terms) by the lies Lucetta told Farfrae and the women of Casterbridge in order for her to protect her relationship with Farfrae. Lucetta and Henchard would have been well matched.

GLOSSARY　　　to the east of Casterbridge … a very fugue of sounds Hardy demonstrates in this paragraph his love of music with his love of Dorset

CHAPTER 42

Enumerate the hints in this chapter that something terrible will happen.

The town council have provided a seed-shop for Elizabeth-Jane and her 'father' and all seems to be going well. Lucetta has faded in the memory of all and Henchard discovers that Elizabeth-Jane and Farfrae have been seeing each other. Henchard discovers a muff and some beads and becomes angry but decides not to say anything to Elizabeth-Jane.

COMMENT   Hardy uses this settled and pleasant chapter as a contrast for the dramatic (see Literary Terms) final chapters. Elizabeth-Jane enjoys 'much serenity' (p. 310).

Farfrae has, despite his fight with Henchard, supported the seed-shop project and the business thrives, which indicates the amount of support in Casterbridge for their previous mayor.

Henchard has changed. Hardy uses 'quite humbly' (p. 309) to describe Henchard's desire for things to remain as they are.

When Henchard discovers the affection of Farfrae for Elizabeth-Jane, all his old hatred is revived as he realises just how much he loves Elizabeth-Jane.

GLOSSARY   **Juno's bird** a peacock

Argus eyes Argus was said to have 100 eyes

solicitus timor anxious fear

locus standi recognised position

CHAPTER 43

Elizabeth-Jane and Farfrae become even more attached and Henchard worries about how he can cope with it. One day Henchard is outside Casterbridge on the top of a hill-fort when he sees Newson returning. Henchard makes hasty plans to leave the district.

After nearly twenty-five years, Henchard, dressed as a hay-trusser, leaves exactly as he had entered.

Compare Henchard's attitude to Newson with Newson's attitude to him.

Again a letter plays an important part in the action, as Elizabeth-Jane is asked to go to Farfrae's house. When Elizabeth-Jane returns there after seeing Henchard off on his travels, she sees Newson sitting there.

She realises this is her real father. She quickly finds it impossible to forgive Henchard's deceit. Elizabeth-Jane and Farfrae prepare for their wedding.

y

THE DOWNFALL OF MICHAEL HENCHARD

COMMENT   Hardy uses the character of Christopher Coney to point
            a clear and wise interpretation of events.

            The reader must feel sorry for Henchard as he leaves
            Casterbridge.

            Lonely and isolated, Henchard is contrasted with the
            promise of a lively well-attended wedding.

            Newson describes Henchard as a 'poor fellow' (p. 324)
            despite the fact that Henchard had obviously done him
            a great disservice.

GLOSSARY   **Mai Dun** Roman hillfort
            via the high road
            Cain Genesis 4: 8–15
            schiedam a Dutch drink

CHAPTER 44

            After travelling fifty miles Henchard arrives back at
            Weydon-Priors and relives the first visit there with Susan
            and the baby. He is unable to stop thinking about
            Elizabeth-Jane and decides to work within a circular
            range of Casterbridge. When he learns of Elizabeth-Jane's
            forthcoming marriage, he buys new clothes and a caged
            goldfinch and determines to return to Casterbridge.

Think why Hardy uses 'good-bye' instead of 'good night'.

At Farfrae's house he loses confidence and enters by a back door. He sees Farfrae and Elizabeth-Jane dancing and completely loses his nerve. She sees him and will not hear him out. She rejects him and he promises never to bother her again. Before she has had time to collect her thoughts Henchard has left. The caged bird is left in the garden.

COMMENT

Hardy again uses Henchard's superstitious nature by implying that he is a victim of a predestined cycle of events. The wheel has come full circle as he returns to Weydon-Priors.

Hardy uses the caged bird as a symbol (see Literary Terms) for Henchard: 'bundle and bird-cage ... a lonely figure on the broad white highway' (p. 331).

There is a dramatic (see Literary Terms) contrast between the merrymaking at the wedding and Henchard's loneliness and isolation.

Henchard is dealt with severely by Elizabeth-Jane whom he has offended with his deception. Her tone is sad and bitter as she impulsively rejects him.

GLOSSARY

pixy-ring ring of darker grass

pari-passu at the same pace

mid might

Martin's day 11 November

the drap a device fitted to a cartwheel to slow it down

A Samson shorn a strong man deprived of his strength (Judges 16: 15–21)

the shade ... upthrown a quote from *The Revolt of Islam* by Shelley – the darkness of his own personality made him want to have Newson's daughter

THE DOWNFALL OF MICHAEL HENCHARD

CHAPTER 45

Consider why it is   Elizabeth-Jane finds the dead goldfinch and is told
Abel Whittle who   several weeks later that Henchard had brought it. She is
cares for Henchard   immediately sorry for the way in which she has treated
in his last hours.   him. She sets out to find him and is just about to give
                         up when she meets Abel Whittle. Abel sadly tells her
                         Henchard's story and takes her to a derelict cottage. He
                         had nursed Henchard until his death which had only
                         been half an hour before. Henchard's will is pencilled
                         on a scrap of paper and pinned to the bedhead.
                         Elizabeth-Jane is very upset by Henchard's death,
                         especially the will that his memory be forgotten.

COMMENT   This chapter is dominated by Whittle's account of his
                 service to Henchard.

                 The influence of the powerful Henchard still exists
                 through his will which is pitifully pinned to his
                 bedhead.

                 Farfrae is willing to forget former differences and
                 quarrels with Henchard and helps Elizabeth-Jane
                 search for him.

                 The dead finch brings an overriding sadness to
                 Elizabeth-Jane; she sees in the gift the symbolism (see
                 Literary Terms) of Henchard's life and good intentions.

                 Elizabeth-Jane searches almost with fanaticism, from
                 Egam Heath to Anglebury.

                 Hardy reintroduces 'poor Whittle' (p. 339) and we are
                 reminded of Whittle's earlier relationship with
                 Henchard. The cottage is described graphically and
                 seems more important than Henchard himself. Hardy
                 cleverly uses dialect (see Literary Terms). We are told
                 that Henchard 'wambled' (p. 341).

When Elizabeth-Jane sees inside the cottage she is shocked into eloquent silence.

Poor Henchard's will is a list of negative directions which serve only to emphasise his own feeling of low self-esteem. Although Elizabeth-Jane is very upset, she agrees to follow Henchard's wishes for his own funeral.

Elizabeth-Jane has matured well beyond her years. Her uncertain upbringing, her true sense of morality, her empathetic disposition all serve to make her the true heroine of the novel. The novel closes upon her secure but still unpredictable future.

GLOSSARY   **antipodean absences** prisons in Australia

Minerva-eyes Minerva was goddess of wisdom

Diana multimammia Diana of the many breasts, goddess of fertility

traps pieces of rickety furniture

Capharnaum where Jesus went to preach 'in the land of the shadow of death' (Isaiah 9: 2)

A *Identify the speaker.*

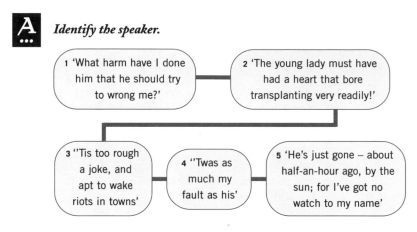

1 'What harm have I done him that he should try to wrong me?'

2 'The young lady must have had a heart that bore transplanting very readily!'

3 ''Tis too rough a joke, and apt to wake riots in towns'

4 ''Twas as much my fault as his'

5 'He's just gone – about half-an-hour ago, by the sun; for I've got no watch to my name'

Identify the person 'to whom' this comment refers.

6 'come in and wet your whistle at my expense for the lift over you have given me'

7 'How will you forgive all my roughness in former days?'

8 'and don't let my sins, when you know them all, cause 'ee to quite forget that though I loved 'ee late I loved 'ee well'

Check your answers on page 87.

B *Consider these issues.*

a Henchard does not approve of Farfrae's courtship of Elizabeth-Jane but vows not to interfere and shows integrity. List other examples of Henchard's sense of integrity.

b How Hardy uses the customers of The Three Mariners in Chapter 43.

c The plot would have changed if Henchard had told Elizabeth-Jane of Newson's visit.

d Henchard looks in at the marriage from a doorway. This 'framing' device is used in other parts of the novel. List as many as you can and say if you think they work.

PART THREE

COMMENTARY

THEMES

SECRECY AND DECEPTION

One of the major themes in the novel is secrecy.

The auction of wife and child is kept 'secret' for twenty years until the furmity woman reveals it. Susan keeps the secret of the auction until her death. The reason for Henchard's oath of abstinence is also a secret. Susan keeps secret the real parentage of Elizabeth-Jane.

Henchard's affair with Lucetta is kept secret from Susan, and Lucetta keeps the affair with Henchard a secret from Farfrae. Hence the importance of Lucetta's letters which result in the fatal skimmington-ride. Henchard keeps the arrival of Newson a secret, and does not tell Elizabeth-Jane.

Smaller 'secrets' are the secret meetings of Susan and Henchard, Elizabeth-Jane and Farfrae, Henchard and Lucetta and Lucetta and Farfrae, the latter leading to their marriage. The villagers plan the skimmington-ride in secret.

FATE

Probably the most obvious theme is the one of fate and coincidence.

Fate takes a hand when the harmless furmity is laced with rum and causes Henchard to auction his wife and child. All may still have been taken as a joke if Newson had not arrived. The following day mother and daughter could possibly have been found, but fate declared Newson's ship to sail to Canada.

Farfrae just happens to stay at The Three Mariners where Susan has a room next door, and where she is able to overhear the conversation. Fate has given Farfrae the power to make the sprouting wheat wholesome and because of this knowledge he is useful to Henchard at this particular time.

Think back and note how many times 'Fate' changes the course of the story.

The national holiday entertainment is spoilt for Henchard because fate declares a wet day and all the inhabitants go to Farfrae's indoor venue. Fate sends the child to Henchard instead of Farfrae and Henchard learns of the true feelings of the people of Casterbridge toward Farfrae.

Ironically (see Literary Terms), Henchard finds out that Elizabeth-Jane is not his real daughter on the very same day he has revealed to her that he is her father.

Henchard's pleas that Elizabeth-Jane will go on living with him come just ten minutes too late: she has decided to become companion to Lucetta.

Farfrae calling on Elizabeth-Jane at High-Place Hall finds Lucetta there instead. Fate intervenes in the budding love of Elizabeth-Jane and Farfrae, Lucetta's attractions overpower Farfrae, and he forgets Elizabeth-Jane.

Fate takes the cruellest turn when the weather prophet forecasts a wet August. Henchard loses all his money by buying up grain and making a loss. Fate brings the furmity woman back to Casterbridge where she tells her story. Fate ensures Farfrae buys up Henchard's business, his home and marries his 'intended', Lucetta. It is fate which takes Jopp to Peter's Finger where he reads the letters, an event which leads to the skimmington-ride and eventually Lucetta's death. When Henchard walks on the Budmouth road to meet Lucetta, it is fate that brings him to the women just as they are about to be mauled by the bull.

It is fate which plays a hand when the effigy rises to the top of the water just as Henchard is about to jump in. It is this vision which makes him change his mind about suicide. It is fate that takes Farfrae and Elizabeth-Jane to find Henchard just half an hour after he has died.

L OVE

Love and a lack of it play an important part in the novel.

When we are introduced to the hay-trusser walking apart from his wife and child pretending to read the ballad paper, we feel a lack of love. The auction confirms this, for although he was drunk he allowed Newson to walk away with his wife and baby.

Even when they are to 'remarry' Henchard is not doing it for love, but simply to put matters right.

The affair between Henchard and Lucetta seems to be one of passion, especially on Lucetta's side with her constant letter-writing. Had Henchard been in love he would probably have married her immediately rather than waiting.

Farfrae's declaration of love for Elizabeth-Jane as he walks her home turns out to be shallow as he is quickly infatuated with Lucetta. Even after her death he realises the true depth of his feelings when he tells us that with Lucetta's death he has exchanged a 'simple sorrow' for prolonged misery: Lucetta's deception would ultimately have ruined the relationship.

Elizabeth-Jane experiences many kinds of love. Identify how they influence the novel.

Elizabeth-Jane is not sure whether she is in love or not at the beginning when she secretly dresses up in her bedroom. The impression she gives us is that she is in love with the idea of being in love. Elizabeth-Jane loves her mother and her mother returns the love with tiger-like protection. This love is shown as the characters are introduced to us walking arm-in-arm along the road. Their affection often seems the only stable love in the novel. Elizabeth-Jane loves Newson. She describes him to Henchard as a kind and loving man. At the end it is clear that she loves Henchard as a father, but cannot get to him to tell him in time.

Abel loves Henchard rather as a spaniel loves his master; despite Henchard's rough treatment of him he stays and cares for Henchard until his death: a sign of genuine affection.

Y

The depth of Farfrae's love for Elizabeth-Jane is uncertain. Farfrae has changed and seems more interested in money than love. Hardy leaves us with Elizabeth-Jane's reflection: 'did not blind her to the fact that there were others receiving less who had deserved much more' (p. 343). Her equanimity, and modesty declared to the last, are certainly not the passionate words of a woman overwhelmingly in love.

AGRICULTURE AND COMMERCE

The background and setting are all vitally important.

Throughout we are given detailed accounts of architecture, street layout, medieval buildings, open roads. The descriptions balance and reflect the incidents and the events. The solitary figures of Henchard and Susan with baby on the open road indicate loneliness and isolation, echoed again at the end when Henchard walks along an open road. The close almost claustrophobic quality of Lucetta's fashionable drawing room seems to suffocate Henchard as he struggles to understand the game she is playing.

The change in the agricultural and commercial ways of life are integral to the novel (see Context & Setting). The whole background is moving, changing and developing. The characters too accept new ways, and new methods. Farfrae's workers are prepared to work longer for less pay.

STRUCTURE

Hardy wrote *The Mayor of Casterbridge* for serial publication in *The Graphic*. This meant he needed to write an exciting event into every edition. When the work was revised for publication in book form some of these incidents were removed.

The first two chapters serve as Prologue (see Literary Terms), with the three Henchards at Weydon Fair and the departure of Michael from the scene. A time lapse of more than eighteen years precedes the middle section and introduces the reader to Casterbridge.

Framings

Hardy links plot to setting. He uses physical features, especially windows, to emphasise the plot. This framing device (see Literary Terms) first appears when Susan and Elizabeth-Jane watch Henchard through the window of The King's Arms; further examples are when Farfrae sings at The Three Mariners, and dramatically, Lucetta seeing the skimmington-ride from the window, and the wedding of Farfrae and Elizabeth-Jane when Henchard looks in from outside.

Timing

Timing is an important element of the structure. There are many examples: the timing of Susan and Elizabeth-Jane's return to Casterbridge just before Henchard's wedding, of Susan's death and of Lucetta's return; the chance meeting of Henchard and Farfrae as he passed through Casterbridge on his way to emigrate. The timing of Newson's appearances and of Henchard's death are all cleverly engineered to add pathos. The way in which the town and countryside are described in such detail gives the characters colour and adds verisimilitude (see Literary Terms) to the novel.

Letters as a structural device

Hardy uses letters as a structural device (see Literary Terms) to accumulate the uncertainty and increase the tension. The letter Susan writes to Henchard is prematurely opened, the letters Lucetta wishes returned are opened; while the mysterious notes to Elizabeth-Jane and Farfrae all add an air of expectation.

Balance of characters

The characters balance each other; their behaviours and personalities each contrasting and illuminating the

Y

other. Farfrae seems to be a direct opposite to Henchard; his pleasant disposition a contrast to Henchard's impulsive temper. The mild Susan and even more pristine Elizabeth-Jane both serve as a foil to the selfish, worldly Lucetta.

Secrets as part of structure
The characters' secrets heighten the suspense. When Henchard marries Susan he does not tell her about Lucetta. Susan does not tell Henchard that Elizabeth-Jane is not his child. Both neglect to tell Elizabeth-Jane of their first marriage. Lucetta keeps her relationship with Henchard a secret and it eventually kills her. Farfrae does not declare to Lucetta that he had once had an attachment to Elizabeth-Jane. All carry on in their lives blissfully ignorant until these facts are revealed, then their behaviours change; love turns to hate.

CHARACTERS

MICHAEL HENCHARD

Henchard, first portrayed as a moody hay-trusser, is a big man, 'a skilled countryman' (p. 1) who walks alongside his wife without communicating with her. Henchard is a character of extremes, either teetotal or drunk; either behaving shamefully as when he auctioned his wife or chivalrously as when he promises Susan a dignified period of courting and remarriage. He either loves or hates as he demonstrates with his treatment of both Farfrae and Elizabeth-Jane.

Henchard's sale of his wife shows that he can be cruel and impulsive, as he also is with Whittle when he oversleeps; and with Jopp when he dismisses him.

Henchard is a man of action rather than words: capable of overpowering emotions and an overzealous idea of

Big man
Naïvely dutiful
and upright
Moody and
impulsive
Lonely

what is right. He shows a creditable sense of responsibility towards Susan, Elizabeth-Jane and Lucetta. Henchard finds it difficult to express his feelings; his brusque, country manners often hiding his true response. He is a mixture of impulsiveness and 'amazing energy' (p. 17).

Henchard is extremely superstitious: he makes his oath with ritualistic majesty in the church. Henchard is a victim of fate: his wife disappears immediately following his drunken auction, he learns to love Elizabeth-Jane just as Newson reappears, and after trying to keep Elizabeth-Jane by telling Newson lies he loses her love and respect.

Henchard has qualities of almost childlike naïveté; he hangs on to the words of the weather prophet, risking a fortune on his advice. He feels that forcing a promise of

Think whether it
was pride or
foolishness which
brought Henchard
to fight with
Farfrae.

marriage from Lucetta will be binding. He pursues poor Abel, guilty only of oversleeping, with massive overreaction. This incident above all others depicts Henchard at his worst. Henchard seems to believe that by tying one hand behind his back he will make the fight 'fair'. Henchard reading to Farfrae from Lucetta's letters also reveals his childlike, spiteful nature; but just like a child he does not take the matter to a full conclusion; he remains unable to take full advantage of Lucetta. The moody, impulsive and petulant side of his nature is contrasted with the hard-working kindly man. Look at Henchard's treatment of Abel Whittle's mother.

Henchard is desperately lonely throughout; he says to Elizabeth-Jane 'to a degree you know nothing of', adding as an afterthought but 'It is my own fault' (p. 302). It is this loneliness which brings him to attempt suicide, and the fear of the ultimate rejection by Elizabeth-Jane which makes him leave Casterbridge, to die an isolated death.

DONALD FARFRAE

Whereas Henchard is a tragic (see Literary Terms) hero, the central figure, Farfrae's role is to act as a contrast to Henchard. Farfrae is 'ruddy and of a fair countenance, bright-eyed and slight of build' (p. 38). Farfrae is a thinking man, slow to react, moderate and sensible. The only immediate reaction we see is his response to Lucetta's advances. This incident proves him to be shallow emotionally, rather than passionate, because he had just declared his affection for Elizabeth-Jane.

Handsome and moderate

Shallow and carefree

Educated and fair-minded

Warm and outgoing

Farfrae embodies the carefree, the bold adventurer. When we are introduced to him he is about to emigrate – a bold audacity seldom witnessed in Casterbridge. Farfrae sings and dances and is warm and outgoing. Farfrae seems genuinely to have the interest of all at heart. This is evidenced when Farfrae tries to give Henchard his furniture back.

Unlike Henchard, Farfrae is educated and able to recognise and appreciate new technology, ideas and systems. He has business acumen, his handling of first Henchard's and then his own affairs is efficient and scrupulously fair.

We doubt Farfrae's ability to be passionately in love; he says of Elizabeth-Jane she is 'pleasing, thrifty and satisfactory' which doesn't suggest unbridled passion. Despite the fact that Farfrae works his men harder and paid them less, he is the town's first choice as a new mayor. He is liked and respected because of his calm, rational and even-tempered demeanour and his absolute fairness in business dealings. He demonstrates the ability to manage people and situations well, as for example in the case of Henchard's intrusion in the royal welcome.

Farfrae seems to be able to forget Henchard's bad behaviour towards him. He bears no resentments and always tries to treat Henchard with friendly generosity. Another example of his empathy and generosity is when Farfrae hires both the old shepherd and his son, in order to prevent the family being split up. Even after his fight with Henchard he is ready to set him up in the seed-shop.

Farfrae is seen as mysterious, we know little of his past. Think whether this influences our opinion of him.

After he has met Lucetta Farfrae seems to change. Although he had half proposed to Elizabeth-Jane he is obviously swept off his feet by Lucetta's fashionable and worldly charms. Although Farfrae is gentle and considerate with Lucetta, he is also enjoying wealth. He buys Henchard's business, his house and furniture. After Lucetta's death we also feel that Farfrae, although genuinely grieved, has an eye on the material benefits from Lucetta's estate.

Farfrae does not seem to have Henchard's sense of duty. Farfrae although half promised to Elizabeth-Jane is able conveniently to forget his declaration of love. After Lucetta's death he resumes his relationship with Elizabeth-Jane. Although the grieving has only been for a year, Farfrae has obviously had mixed feelings about her death; he felt 'he had exchanged a looming misery for a simple sorrow' (p. 309).

Throughout, Farfrae acts as a contrast to Henchard, and although we feel sorry for Henchard when he makes mistakes and acts hastily we do not feel the same compassion for Farfrae. The novel ends as it began with Henchard in a central position.

ELIZABETH-JANE

*Sensible and
level-headed*

*Shrewd and
reflective*

Caring

Elizabeth-Jane is portrayed from the first as being sensible and level-headed. Hardy almost criticises her, 'a girl characterised by earnestness and soberness of vision' (p. 56). It is she who organises her mother, takes on the role of waitress in order to pay their bill at The Three Mariners.

Elizabeth-Jane is portrayed as reflective, calm and organised. She seems not to mind her mother's 'marriage' to Henchard or even to panic at her mother's very serious illness. Elizabeth-Jane's well-balanced and philosophical approach to life could easily be a result of her reading. She is the only character who possesses books; these are more important to her than fine clothes.

Elizabeth-Jane is an observer to many scenes, indeed much of the interpretation is through her eyes. She is a shrewd evaluator of human behaviour. It is she who warns Henchard not to employ Jopp, and because of her concern that her 'father' would get into trouble she warns Farfrae of Henchard's vindictive nature. She stands by Henchard when he is down on his luck and cares and looks after him. She plays the same role for Lucetta, endeavouring to protect her by stopping her seeing the skimmington-ride. Whereas Farfrae's love for Elizabeth-Jane seems only to be superficial to begin with, Henchard's love for her is almost an obsession.

Hardy sees Elizabeth-Jane as innocent, good and simple. She is portrayed as having positive qualities. Her sensitivity and practical common sense combine to make a stable but passionless figure. Her strict adherence to moral codes is evident throughout the novel. This contrasts with Lucetta's characteristics.

SUSAN NEWSON/HENCHARD

Passive
Secretive
Dutiful

Susan is very much a grey shadow of a figure in the novel, very passive, her life seems to happen to her, she does not apparently have choice. Yet Susan does display some strength of character; she flings her wedding ring at Henchard and leaves with the sailor Newson. She also insists that Elizabeth-Jane keeps the name Newson, but does not tell her why it is important. Susan is a woman well able to keep secrets.

Susan seems to want very little of life; her return to Casterbridge was on account of Elizabeth-Jane not for her own needs; although by the time they reached Casterbridge she was very ill.

It could be said that Susan was sly to conceal Elizabeth-Jane's true father, but we are aware of Henchard's violent temper. Susan was probably concerned at the difference which this revelation would make before her remarriage. She could anticipate that this knowledge would jeopardise the marriage and then Elizabeth-Jane would be homeless.

The letter from Susan to Henchard gives a fuller picture of her character development. Throughout we feel nothing but pity for Susan, a victim of fate and circumstance, naively believing that her being sold to Newson was a binding contract equal to that of marriage. Even her death – only months before Newson visited Casterbridge – was sadly premature. Poor Susan's last wishes were that the ounce pennies should not be spent, but buried with her, and even this simple request did not take place.

LUCETTA TEMPLEMAN/LE SUEUR

Exotic and sophisticated

Selfish and self-seeking

Lucetta is introduced as an exotic, romantic figure. Her affair with Henchard, which would have shocked Victorian readers, intrigues us. The mystery is also emphasised by the fact that she is first Lucetta Le Sueur and then changes her name to Templeman.

Lucetta appears selfish from the first. She is fashionable, gay, flirtatious and self-seeking. Her previous association with Henchard was symbiotic, both characters impulsive and quick to react. Both she and Henchard are prepared to use others to their own advantage. Lucetta invites Elizabeth-Jane to live with her because she feels this will attract Henchard to High-Place Hall. Henchard uses Farfrae to help his business, but he, just like Lucetta, with Elizabeth-Jane, quickly becomes jealous, and both characters are prepared to get rid of those they have used without a second thought. Ironically (see Literary Terms), Henchard abandons Lucetta when Susan returns and Lucetta abandons Henchard after meeting Farfrae.

Lucetta's letters are vital to the plot, concealed in Henchard's house, partly read to Farfrae, and eventually read to the assembled audience in Peter's Finger.

Lucetta's habits of writing letters and expressing her innermost thoughts and feelings eventually bring about her downfall. Lucetta is not described in detail by Hardy. She is almost a stereotype (see Literary Terms) of misfortune. Her letters and secret meetings with Henchard lead us to the discovery of their unfortunate affair. As the reader's sympathy for her reaches a climax, she dies, thereby removing our further sympathy – and moral judgement.

RICHARD NEWSON

Richard Newson appears fortuitously at the furmity tent and considers that Susan and the baby would be better off with him. He says little, and we only learn about him in the following twenty years by Susan and Elizabeth-Jane's account, that he was a kind and caring father and husband.

Extrovert

Genial and caring

When he appears later at Peter's Finger, he adds an atmosphere (see Literary Terms) of mystery. He appears to the regulars good-humoured and extrovert, willing to contribute to the skimmington-ride. He is ready to believe Henchard when he is told of his wife and daughters' deaths, and when he discovers the deception is still ready to believe well of Henchard: "'Twas as much my fault as his, poor fellow' (p. 324). This indicates a geniality of nature and a power of forgiveness comparable only with Farfrae.

MINOR CHARACTERS

Abel Whittle

Though minor, Abel plays an important part in the novel. We first see him in trouble with Henchard for not getting up in the morning and he is taken from his home without his breeches. Farfrae protects Abel from ridicule and this becomes the beginning of a quarrel between Farfrae and Henchard.

It is ironic (see Literary Terms) that it is Abel who cares for Henchard at the end of his life. As Abel Whittle recounts the story of Henchard's illness and death we are reminded of Henchard's good points, especially the kindness shown to Whittle's mother.

The furmity woman

Solomon Longways

Christopher Coney

Buzzford

Mother Cuxsom

Nance Mockridge

These are often referred to as the urban chorus or the rural inhabitants.

Their role in the novel is to add information, which the reader may not otherwise have. They gossip and give opinions. They view the scene and evaluate it for us, and provide yet another perspective.

Hardy uses his characters to add realism, humour and warmth to the plot.

All add a colour to the proceedings. It is Nance Mockridge who complains of the bread.

Hardy uses these characters to remind us that there is another social stratum in Casterbridge. The inhabitants of Mixen Lane congregate around Peter's Finger. Even here Hardy shows contrast. Charles would have robbed Newson of his gold, but Coney and Longways send a note to Farfrae to take him out of the way before the skimmington-ride. Mother Cuxsom, always jolly, contrasts with the vicious Nance.

Yet here we see true humanity. They all attend weddings and funerals, enjoy themselves on the national holiday, are able to forgive and forget and then move forward in their restricted lives.

LANGUAGE & STYLE

Hardy is able to use a mixture of 'voices': the narrator (see Literary Terms) and often the bystander giving us a view of the scene, but often also an opinion as well. Hardy constantly changes the viewpoint, his style and technique. Overall it must be remembered that the novel was once designed in events of equal length for serialisation. This gives a balanced feeling to the whole. At the beginning of the book the novelist plays the outsider, the narrator, giving us a view of the events. We are told of the family walking on a dusty road and that what 'would have attracted the attention of any casual observer disposed to overlook them, was the perfect silence they preserved' (p. 1). Then Hardy moves closer in to observe the baby, 'a tiny girl in short clothes and knitted yarn' (p. 2). He uses windows, doorways etc. to 'frame' his pictures and focus our attention.

Hardy uses some images more than once so as to contrast an event. List as many as you can remember.

Hardy uses many visual effects or images (see Literary Terms), and in a variety of ways. The importance of a scene is emphasised by describing it in exquisite detail. He uses the detailed description of Casterbridge, snug, safe and secure with its historical monuments, as a contrast to the open roads and the Ring: 'Its squareness was, indeed, the characteristic which most struck the eye in this antiquated borough, the borough of Casterbridge – at that time, recent as it was, untouched by the faintest sprinkle of modernism' (p. 26).

The sense of the town and its surroundings' security is immediate. Contrast this with 'the dismal privacy which the eastern circle [of the Ring] enforced' (p. 73). We feel immediately a sense of fear and foreboding, especially when this is followed with a more detailed description, 'bearded with withered bents that formed waves under the brush of the wind' (p. 74). The alliterative (see Literary Terms) effect emphasises the lonely isolation of the characters about to meet there.

The bustling life of Casterbridge is also shown: 'In addition to these fixed obstacles which spoke so cheerfully of individual unrestraint as to boundaries, movables occupied the path and roadway to a perplexing extent' (p. 61), and he goes on to describe the traffic and the occupants of Casterbridge going about their business.

Hardy uses dialogue to paint the characters of Casterbridge most vividly. By using dialect (see Literary

Terms) he is able to add warmth, humour, anger and
distress. Dialogue appeases Hardy's sense of the
dramatic (see Literary Terms), and has subsequently
made his plays easier to dramatise and undoubtedly
more realistic.

Dialect is used to
colour the picture
Hardy paints.
Think of the best
example of this.

Hardy as narrator (see Literary Terms) is controlled,
intelligent and educated, whereas the dialect (see
Literary Terms) used by his characters often reflects
their lack of education. An example of this is when
Jopp tells Henchard of Farfrae's purchase of his house,
and at Henchard's obvious surprise, Jopp replies, 'Well,
as somebody was sure to live there, and you couldn't, it
can do 'ee no harm that he's the man' (p. 230). Contrast
this with the narrator's voice: 'Henchard turned slightly
and saw that the comer was Jopp, his old foreman, now
employed elsewhere, to whom, though he hated him, he
had gone for lodgings because Jopp was the one man in
Casterbridge whose observation and opinion the fallen
corn-merchant despised to the point of indifference' (p.
230).

Frequently Hardy's use of language is almost poetic: 'the
click of a lock' (p. 47) and 'sifting and rustling' (p. 47).
He also uses visual imagery (see Literary Terms): 'airy
spheres of thistledown floated into the same street …
innumerable tawny and yellow leaves skimmed along
the pavement, and stole through people's doorways into
their passages with a hesitating scratch on the floor, like
the skirts of timid visitors' (p. 58).

The use of the extended metaphor, the simile,
alliteration (see Literary Terms) all in one paragraph
demonstrates the greatness of Hardy as a writer.

PART FOUR

STUDY SKILLS

HOW TO USE QUOTATIONS

One of the secrets of success in writing essays is the way you use quotations. There are five basic principles:

- Put inverted commas at the beginning and end of the quotation
- Write the quotation exactly as it appears in the orginal
- Do not use a quotation that repeats what you have just written
- Use the quotation so that it fits into your sentence
- Keep the quotation as short as possible

Quotations should be used to develop the line of thought in your essays. Your comment should not duplicate what is in your quotation. For example:

Henchard, after waking from his drunken sleep, discovers he has sold his wife and baby to a sailor.
'She's gone – to be sure she is – gone with that sailor who bought her, and Elizabeth-Jane'.

Far more effective is to write:

Henchard, waking, recalls how in a drunken stupor the night before he had auctioned his wife and child: 'She's gone ... with that sailor, and Elizabeth-Jane'.

The most sophisticated way of using the writer's words is to embed them into your sentence:

Henchard, waking, recalls how in a drunken stupor the night before he had auctioned his wife and Elizabeth-Jane to 'that sailor' and now 'She's gone'.

When you use quotations in this way, you are demonstating the ability to use text as evidence to support your ideas – not simply including words from the original to prove you have read it.

Everyone writes differently. Work through the suggestions given here and adapt the advice to suit your own style and interests. This will improve your essay-writing skills and allow your personal voice to emerge.

The following points indicate in ascending order the skills of essay writing:

- Picking out one or two facts about the story and adding the odd detail
- Writing about the text by retelling the story
- Retelling the story and adding a quotation here and there
- Organising an answer which explains what is happening in the text and giving quotations to support what you write

. . . .

- Writing in such a way as to show that you have thought about the intentions of the writer of the text and that you understand the techniques used
- Writing at some length, giving your viewpoint on the text and commenting by picking out details to support your views
- Looking at the text as a work of art, demonstrating clear critical judgement and explaining to the reader of your essay how the enjoyment of the text is assisted by literary devices, linguistic effects and psychological insights; showing how the text relates to the time when it was written

The dotted line above represents the division between lower- and higher-level grades. Higher-level performance begins when you start to consider your reponse as a reader of the text. The highest level is reached when you offer an enthusiastic personal response and show how this piece of literature is a product of its time.

Coursework essay

Set aside an hour or so at the start of your work to plan what you have to do.

- List all the points you feel are needed to cover the task. Collect page references of information and quotations that will support what you have to say. A helpful tool is the highlighter pen: this saves painstaking copying and enables you to target precisely what you want to use.
- Focus on what you consider to be the main points of the essay. Try to sum up your argument in a single sentence, which could be the closing sentence of your essay. Depending on the essay title, it could be a statement about a character: Our first impression of Donald Farfrae is 'He was ruddy and of a fair countenance, bright-eyed, and slight in build'. At first he seemed to be merely passing through Caster-bridge; an opinion about a setting: The agricultural setting of *The Mayor of Casterbridge* is more than mere background: it is an integral part of the plot; or a judgement on a theme: Secrecy is one of the main themes, and both disclosure of a secret and failure to disclose a secret are causes of Henchard's downfall.
- Make a short essay plan. Use the first paragraph to introduce the argument you wish to make. In the following paragraphs develop this argument with details, examples and other possible points of view. Sum up your argument in the last paragraph. Check you have answered the question.
- Write the essay, remembering all the time the central point you are making.
- On completion, go back over what you have written to eliminate careless errors and improve expression. Read it aloud to yourself, or, if you are feeling more confident, to a relative or friend.

If you can, try to type your essay, using a word processor. This will allow you to correct and improve your writing without spoiling its appearance.

Examination essay

The essay written in an examination often carries more marks than the coursework essay even though it is written under considerable time pressure.

In the revision period build up notes on various aspects of the text you are using. Fortunately, in acquiring this set of York Notes on *The Mayor of Casterbridge*, you have made a prudent beginning! York Notes are set out to give you vital information and help you to construct your personal overview of the text.

Make notes with appropriate quotations about the key issues of the set text. Go into the examination knowing your text and having a clear set of opinions about it.

In most English Literature examinations, you can take in copies of your set books. This is an enormous advantage although it may lull you into a false sense of security. Beware! There is simply not enough time in an examination to read the book from scratch.

In the examination

- Read the question paper carefully and remind yourself what you have to do
- Look at the questions on your set texts to select the one that most interests you and mentally work out the points you wish to stress
- Remind yourself of the time available and how you are going to use it
- Briefly map out a short plan in note form that will keep your writing on track and illustrate the key argument you want to make
- Then set about writing it
- When you have finished, check through to eliminate errors

To summarise,
these are the
keys to success

- **Know the text**
- **Have a clear understanding of and opinions on the storyline, characters, setting, themes and writer's concerns**
- **Select the right material**
- **Plan and write a clear response, continually bearing the question in mind**

SAMPLE ESSAY PLAN

A typical essay question on *The Major of Casterbridge* is followed by a sample essay plan in note form. This does not present the only answer to the question, merely one answer. Do not be afraid to include your own ideas, and leave out some of those in the sample! Remember that quotations are essential to prove and illustrate the points you make.

Many would say that Michael Henchard brought all his troubles upon himself. Would you agree?

Introduction

Henchard's character is complex: made up of a mixture of positive and negative traits.

Part 1

He is impulsive, quick-tempered, belligerent, but he does attempt to control his violent behaviour: taking an oath not to drink; avoiding women in Casterbridge (yet not in Jersey); attempting to live a good life as a mayor, churchwarden and magistrate.

Part 2

Henchard is able to demonstrate finer feelings: his readiness to make Susan his wife and take Elizabeth-Jane as his daughter; his ready friendship with Donald Farfrae to begin with; openness and honesty; readiness to do the right thing by Lucetta; sense of integrity; does not divulge Lucetta's letters; ties arm for a 'fair fight'.

Part 3

But Henchard is a victim of superstition, fate and coincidence: the holiday festival – rain spoils his event;

Fall's prediction is wrong and bankrupts Henchard; Lucetta arrives as Susan dies; the opening of Susan's letter; the lie to Newson; Farfrae's buying not only his business but home and marrying Lucetta.

Conclusion All the above add anger, anguish and jealousy to the life of a man who has taken a turn for the worse and drinking heavily is destined for disaster.

FURTHER QUESTIONS

Make a plan as shown above and attempt these questions.

1 Compare the characters of Elizabeth-Jane and Lucetta. Discuss the importance of Elizabeth-Jane in the novel.

2 Which do you consider to be the two most moving scenes and why?

3 Letters play an important part in this novel. What part do they play in the plot?

4 Secrecy is a major theme in the novel. Identify the secrets and discuss their effect on the plot.

5 Elizabeth-Jane is aware that good fortune is 'extremely fickle'. How far does Hardy demonstrate this in *A Mayor of Casterbridge*?

6 What significance does 'place' play in the novel? Refer to some of these places in your answer: Weydon-Priors Fair, High-Place Hall, Peter's Finger, the derelict cottage, the bull ring.

7 Henchard and Farfrae are very different. Discuss the ways in which their characters differ.

8 Hardy uses 'coincidence' as a means of developing the plot. How effective is this?

9 How does Hardy develop our sympathy for Henchard?

10 What part do the minor characters play in the novel? Refer to at least two of the following characters in your answer: The furmity woman, Abel Whittle, Christopher Coney, Jopp.

PART FIVE

CULTURAL CONNECTIONS

BROADER PERSPECTIVES

A useful device to place the novel in its social and
historical context is to look at the BBC video,
dramatised by Dennis Potter. However, read the novel
first. Many sequences are not in the same order on the
video as in the novel. For example, the first scene on
video features Susan and a grown-up Elizabeth-Jane,
not Henchard and Susan nineteen years before. This is
important as this time lapse (although dealt with as a
retrospective view on the video) forms an important
prologue to the text. Small details differ from the text,
such as the proposed drowning of Henchard. The video
is ideal for costume, environment and lifestyle. You will
be able to 'see' the story, and it also helps show how the
dialogue brings life to the characters. You will be able to
'hear' the characters speak.

The following books are useful for a more detailed
literary criticism:

R.P. Draper's *Hardy: the Tragic Novels* (Macmillan,
1975); D. Bram's *Thomas Hardy: The Mayor of
Casterbridge* (Edward Arnold); and, for regional
information, D. Kay-Robinson's *Hardy's Wessex
Reappraised* (David & Charles, 1972)

Many biographies of Thomas Hardy have been written.
You may enjoy F.E. Hardy's *The Life of Thomas Hardy
1840–1928* (Macmillan, 1962).

alliteration the same sound repeated

ambiguity to have a double meaning

ambivalence to have two different views or feelings about the same thing

anticlimax a sudden effect of banality or ordinariness

antithesis an opposite or contradicting idea

atmosphere mood and setting

denote to signify or mark out

device any literary method or technique can be called a device

dialect local way of speaking

drama the action of the play/novel

flashback technique a sudden jump back in time to an earlier period or event

image a word 'picture' – something which conjures up a picture

irony saying one thing whilst meaning another

metaphor where one thing is described as being another

monologue scene in drama where one person speaks alone

narrator the story teller

onomatopoeia where words sound like the noise which they describe

parody an imitation designed to mock or ridicule

persona character

prologue the introductory section of work

satire where people appear ridiculous or contemptible

simile comparing two things using 'as' or 'like'

soliloquy when a character speaks alone, out aloud to themselves

stereotype a fixed idea or standard, mental impression

symbol where one thing is used to act or stand for another

tragedy traces the downfall of a character

verisimilitude the believability of a sequence or story

TEST YOURSELF (Chapters 1–5)

A 1 Henchard
2 Newson
3 Henchard (about Susan)
4 Henchard
5 Henchard
6 Henchard

TEST YOURSELF (Chapters 6–12)

A 1 Susan Henchard
2 Elizabeth-Jane
3 Henchard
4 Michael Henchard
5 Michael Henchard
6 Farfrae

TEST YOURSELF (Chapters 13–22)

A 1 Henchard
2 Henchard
3 Elizabeth-Jane
4 Elizabeth-Jane
5 Lucetta

6 Henchard (and his marriage to Susan)
7 Elizabeth-Jane

TEST YOURSELF (Chapters 23–33)

A 1 Lucetta
2 Furmity woman (Mrs Goodenough)
3 Lucetta
4 Solomon Longways
5 Farfrae
6 Farfrae
7 Lucetta

TEST YOURSELF (Chapters 34–45)

A 1 Farfrae
2 Farfrae
3 Longways
4 Newson
5 Abel Whittle
6 Newson
7 Henchard
8 Henchard

NOTES

NOTES

NOTES

GCSE and equivalent levels (£3.50 each)

Maya Angelou
I Know Why the Caged Bird Sings

Jane Austen
Pride and Prejudice

Alan Ayckbourn
Absent Friends

Elizabeth Barrett Browning
Selected Poems

Robert Bolt
A Man for All Seasons

Harold Brighouse
Hobson's Choice

Charlotte Brontë
Jane Eyre

Emily Brontë
Wuthering Heights

Shelagh Delaney
A Taste of Honey

Charles Dickens
David Copperfield

Charles Dickens
Great Expectations

Charles Dickens
Hard Times

Charles Dickens
Oliver Twist

Roddy Doyle
Paddy Clarke Ha Ha Ha

George Eliot
Silas Marner

George Eliot
The Mill on the Floss

William Golding
Lord of the Flies

Oliver Goldsmith
She Stoops To Conquer

Willis Hall
The Long and the Short and the Tall

Thomas Hardy
Far from the Madding Crowd

Thomas Hardy
The Mayor of Casterbridge

Thomas Hardy
Tess of the d'Urbervilles

Thomas Hardy
The Withered Arm and other Wessex Tales

L.P. Hartley
The Go-Between

Seamus Heaney
Selected Poems

Susan Hill
I'm the King of the Castle

Barry Hines
A Kestrel for a Knave

Louise Lawrence
Children of the Dust

Harper Lee
To Kill a Mockingbird

Laurie Lee
Cider with Rosie

Arthur Miller
The Crucible

Arthur Miller
A View from the Bridge

Robert O'Brien
Z for Zachariah

Frank O'Connor
My Oedipus Complex and other stories

George Orwell
Animal Farm

J.B. Priestley
An Inspector Calls

Willy Russell
Educating Rita

Willy Russell
Our Day Out

J.D. Salinger
The Catcher in the Rye

William Shakespeare
Henry IV Part 1

William Shakespeare
Henry V

William Shakespeare
Julius Caesar

William Shakespeare
Macbeth

William Shakespeare
The Merchant of Venice

William Shakespeare
A Midsummer Night's Dream

William Shakespeare
Much Ado About Nothing

William Shakespeare
Romeo and Juliet

William Shakespeare
The Tempest

William Shakespeare
Twelfth Night

George Bernard Shaw
Pygmalion

Mary Shelley
Frankenstein

R.C. Sherriff
Journey's End

Rukshana Smith
Salt on the snow

John Steinbeck
Of Mice and Men

Robert Louis Stevenson
Dr Jekyll and Mr Hyde

Jonathan Swift
Gulliver's Travels

Robert Swindells
Daz 4 Zoe

Mildred D. Taylor
Roll of Thunder, Hear My Cry

Mark Twain
Huckleberry Finn

James Watson
Talking in Whispers

William Wordsworth
Selected Poems

A Choice of Poets

Mystery Stories of the Nineteenth Century including The Signalman

Nineteenth Century Short Stories

Poetry of the First World War

Six Women Poets

York Notes Advanced (£3.99 each)

Margaret Atwood
The Handmaid's Tale

Jane Austen
Mansfield Park

Jane Austen
Persuasion

Jane Austen
Pride and Prejudice

Alan Bennett
Talking Heads

William Blake
Songs of Innocence and of Experience

Charlotte Brontë
Jane Eyre

Emily Brontë
Wuthering Heights

Geoffrey Chaucer
The Franklin's Tale

Geoffrey Chaucer
General Prologue to the Canterbury Tales

Geoffrey Chaucer
The Wife of Bath's Prologue and Tale

Joseph Conrad
Heart of Darkness

Charles Dickens
Great Expectations

John Donne
Selected Poems

George Eliot
The Mill on the Floss

F. Scott Fitzgerald
The Great Gatsby

E.M. Forster
A Passage to India

Brian Friel
Translations

Thomas Hardy
The Mayor of Casterbridge

Thomas Hardy
Tess of the d'Urbervilles

Seamus Heaney
Selected Poems from Opened Ground

Nathaniel Hawthorne
The Scarlet Letter

James Joyce
Dubliners

John Keats
Selected Poems

Christopher Marlowe
Doctor Faustus

Arthur Miller
Death of a Salesman

Toni Morrison
Beloved

William Shakespeare
Antony and Cleopatra

William Shakespeare
As You Like It

William Shakespeare
Hamlet

William Shakespeare
King Lear

William Shakespeare
Measure for Measure

William Shakespeare
The Merchant of Venice

William Shakespeare
Much Ado About Nothing

William Shakespeare
Othello

William Shakespeare
Romeo and Juliet

William Shakespeare
The Tempest

William Shakespeare
The Winter's Tale

Mary Shelley
Frankenstein

Alice Walker
The Color Purple

Oscar Wilde
The Importance of Being Earnest

Tennessee Williams
A Streetcar Named Desire

John Webster
The Duchess of Malfi

W.B. Yeats
Selected Poems

Chinua Achebe
Things Fall Apart

Edward Albee
Who's Afraid of Virginia Woolf?

Margaret Atwood
Cat's Eye

Jane Austen
Emma

Jane Austen
Northanger Abbey

Jane Austen
Sense and Sensibility

Samuel Beckett
Waiting for Godot

Robert Browning
Selected Poems

Robert Burns
Selected Poems

Angela Carter
Nights at the Circus

Geoffrey Chaucer
The Merchant's Tale

Geoffrey Chaucer
The Miller's Tale

Geoffrey Chaucer
The Nun's Priest's Tale

Samuel Taylor Coleridge
Selected Poems

Daniel Defoe
Moll Flanders

Daniel Defoe
Robinson Crusoe

Charles Dickens
Bleak House

Charles Dickens
Hard Times

Emily Dickinson
Selected Poems

Carol Ann Duffy
Selected Poems

George Eliot
Middlemarch

T.S. Eliot
The Waste Land

T.S. Eliot
Selected Poems

Henry Fielding
Joseph Andrews

E.M. Forster
Howards End

John Fowles
The French Lieutenant's Woman

Robert Frost
Selected Poems

Elizabeth Gaskell
North and South

Stella Gibbons
Cold Comfort Farm

Graham Greene
Brighton Rock

Thomas Hardy
Jude the Obscure

Thomas Hardy
Selected Poems

Joseph Heller
Catch-22

Homer
The Iliad

Homer
The Odyssey

Gerard Manley Hopkins
Selected Poems

Aldous Huxley
Brave New World

Kazuo Ishiguro
The Remains of the Day

Ben Jonson
The Alchemist

Ben Jonson
Volpone

James Joyce
A Portrait of the Artist as a Young Man

Philip Larkin
Selected Poems

D.H. Lawrence
The Rainbow

D.H. Lawrence
Selected Stories

D.H. Lawrence
Sons and Lovers

D.H. Lawrence
Women in Love

John Milton
Paradise Lost Bks I & II

John Milton
Paradise Lost Bks IV & IX

Thomas More
Utopia

Sean O'Casey
Juno and the Paycock

George Orwell
Nineteen Eighty-four

John Osborne
Look Back in Anger

Wilfred Owen
Selected Poems

Sylvia Plath
Selected Poems

Alexander Pope
Rape of the Lock and other poems

Ruth Prawer Jhabvala
Heat and Dust

Jean Rhys
Wide Sargasso Sea

William Shakespeare
As You Like It

William Shakespeare
Coriolanus

William Shakespeare
Henry IV Pt 1

William Shakespeare
Henry V

William Shakespeare
Julius Caesar

William Shakespeare
Macbeth

William Shakespeare
Measure for Measure

William Shakespeare
A Midsummer Night's Dream

William Shakespeare
Richard II

William Shakespeare
Richard III

William Shakespeare
Sonnets

William Shakespeare
The Taming of the Shrew

William Shakespeare
Twelfth Night

William Shakespeare
The Winter's Tale

George Bernard Shaw
Arms and the Man

George Bernard Shaw
Saint Joan

Muriel Spark
The Prime of Miss Jean Brodie

John Steinbeck
The Grapes of Wrath

John Steinbeck
The Pearl

Tom Stoppard
Arcadia

Tom Stoppard
Rosencrantz and Guildenstern are Dead

Jonathan Swift
Gulliver's Travels and The Modest Proposal

Alfred, Lord Tennyson
Selected Poems

W.M. Thackeray
Vanity Fair

Virgil
The Aeneid

Edith Wharton
The Age of Innocence

Tennessee Williams
Cat on a Hot Tin Roof

Tennessee Williams
The Glass Menagerie

Virginia Woolf
Mrs Dalloway

Virginia Woolf
To the Lighthouse

William Wordsworth
Selected Poems

Metaphysical Poets

York Notes – the Ultimate Literature Guides

York Notes are recognised as the best literature study guides.
If you have enjoyed using this book and have found it useful, you
can now order others directly from us – simply follow the ordering
instructions below.

HOW TO ORDER

Decide which title(s) you require and then order in one of the following
ways:

Booksellers
All titles available from good bookstores.

By post
List the title(s) you require in the space provided overleaf,
select your method of payment, complete your name and
address details and return your completed order form and
payment to:

Addison Wesley Longman Ltd
PO BOX 88
Harlow
Essex CM19 5SR

By phone
Call our Customer Information Centre on 01279 623923 to
place your order, quoting mail number: HEYN1.

By fax
Complete the order form overleaf, ensuring you fill in your
name and address details and method of payment, and fax it
to us on 01279 414130.

By e-mail
E-mail your order to us on awlhe.orders@awl.co.uk listing
title(s) and quantity required and providing full name and
address details as requested overleaf. Please quote mail
number: HEYN1. Please do not send credit card details by
e-mail.

York Notes Order Form

Titles required:

Quantity   Title/ISBN   Price

_____

_____

_____

_____

_____

_____

_____

Sub total _____

Please add £2.50 postage & packing _____

(_P & P is free for orders over £50_) _____

Total _____

| Mail no: HEYN1 |

Your Name _____

Your Address _____

_____

Postcode _____   Telephone _____

Method of payment

☐ I enclose a cheque or a P/O for £_____ made payable to
Addison Wesley Longman Ltd

☐ Please charge my Visa/Access/AMEX/Diners Club card
Number _____   Expiry Date _____
Signature _____   Date _____

(please ensure that the address given above is the same as for your credit card)

Prices and other details are correct at time of going to press but may change without notice.
All orders are subject to status.

☐ _Please tick this box if you_
would like a complete listing of
Longman Study Guides
(suitable for GCSE and A-level students)

York Press

Longman

Addison
Wesley
Longman